Scottish Executive Health Department

Fair Shares for All

Final Report

The National Review of Resource Allocation for the NHS in Scotland

CONTENTS

NATIONAL REVIEW OF RESOURCE ALLOCATION 1

INTRODUCTION 1

EXECUTIVE SUMMARY 3

    The Data 3

    Stability 3

    Transparency 3

    'Arbuthnott index' 4

    Demography 6

    Remoteness 7

    General Medical Services (GMS) 7

    Results 7

    Conclusions 10

CHAPTER 1:
RESPONSE TO COMMENTS ABOUT THE BASIC METHODS IN *FAIR SHARES FOR ALL* 12

    a) The Remit 12

    b) A Single Formula for All Health Boards 12

    c) Analysis at Care Programme Level 13

    d) The Use of Evidence Based on Recent Patterns of Care 14

    e) The Use of Small Area Data 15

    f) Quality of Data 16

    g) Range of Services Covered in the Review 16

    h) Incentives for Health Boards 18

    i) The Adjustment for Remoteness 18

    j) Anomalies Between Health Boards 18

    k) Scale of Redistribution 19

    l) The Complexity of the Formula 19

CHAPTER 2:
POPULATION ESTIMATES AND ADJUSTMENTS FOR AGE AND SEX 20

    Population 20

    Adjustment for Population Age and Sex 23

CHAPTER 3:
MORBIDITY AND LIFE CIRCUMSTANCES 25

    An Alternative Approach 26

    Results 34

    Conclusions 36

CHAPTER 4:
REMOTENESS 38

    Other Indicators 39

    Island Health Boards 41

    A Uniform Adjustment for the Three Island Health Boards 41

    Implications for Mainland Health Boards 42

    Quality of Evidence 43

CHAPTER 5:
RESULTS FOR HOSPITAL AND COMMUNITY HEALTH SERVICES AND GP PRESCRIBING 44

Relative Needs..44
Changes from Current Allocation Shares...45
Implications for Health Board Allocations...46
Progress Towards New Target Shares...48
Conclusions...48

CHAPTER 6:
GENERAL MEDICAL SERVICES 49

Relevance of a Resource Allocation Formula to GMS 49
Revised formula for GMS..51
Overall Results..54
Steering Group Recommendations for GMS...56

CHAPTER 7:
UPDATING THE FORMULA 57

Population Shares...57
Conclusions...59

ANNEX A:
CONTRIBUTION TO THE CONSULTATION OF THE NATIONAL REVIEW
OF RESOURCE ALLOCATION 60

Health Boards...60
NHS Trusts..60
Others..61

ANNEX B:
LIST OF MEMBERSHIP OF GROUPS...63

Steering Group..63
Reference Group..64
GMS Sub Group...65

ANNEX C:
THE CHOICE OF POPULATION COUNT 66

Advice from the General Register Office for Scotland on the Population Count 66
Analysis of Recent Trends in Population Data..67

ANNEX D:
ADJUSTMENTS FOR AGE AND SEX 71

ANNEX E: MORBIDITY AND LIFE CIRCUMSTANCES 76

Small Area Analysis..76
Measurement of Population at Small Area Level..78
Measurement of Supply...78
Year on Year Stability of the Models..81
Community Health Services...83

ANNEX F: THE 'ARBUTHNOTT INDEX' 84

ANNEX G: GLOSSARY OF ACRONYMS..86

NATIONAL REVIEW OF RESOURCE ALLOCATION
INTRODUCTION

1.   The National Review of Resource Allocation was set up in December 1997 to advise on methods of allocating National Health Service resources between Health Boards in Scotland. The results of this review, which was carried out by a Steering Group chaired by Professor Sir John Arbuthnott, are set out in the report, *Fair Shares for All*, that was issued for consultation in July 1999. Some 90 responses were received during consultation and a list of those who provided comments is given in Annex A. In addition, the Health and Community Care Committee of the Scottish Parliament issued a report on *Fair Shares for All*. In response to this consultation the Minister for Health and Community Care, Susan Deacon, asked Sir John Arbuthnott to reconvene the Steering Group to consider the comments received, to carry out any further work required to address these comments, and

to provide revised recommendations to her by 30 June 2000. This report outlines the further work carried out by the Steering Group

2.   The Steering Group is most grateful for the very detailed, thorough and constructive comments provided during consultation, especially by the Health and Community Care Committee. In response to these comments the Steering Group has carried out a careful review of the data, the methods of analysis, and the results. To help it address these issues two other groups were set up: a Reference Group to advise on technical issues, and a group on General Medical Services, one of the more complex areas in the review of resource allocation. The membership of these groups is given in Annex B.

3.   There are several points that the Steering Group wish to emphasise at the outset. *Fair Shares for All* was the first major review of the allocation formula used in the NHS in over 20 years. In the foreword to that report, Sir John Arbuthnott explained that the report "seeks to turn a new page in the resourcing of our Health Service in Scotland". The Steering Group was convinced that there was a clear need for a new evidence-based approach to the allocation of resources between Health Boards. The current formula that is used to allocate resources lacks an evidence base and takes only limited account of the influence of deprivation and remoteness on the relative need for healthcare resources. **None of the comments received during consultation sought to defend the current method of allocating resources**.

4.   The key objectives of the Steering Group have been:

- to establish a fair method of sharing resources between Health Boards; and
- to base this method as far as possible on evidence about the relative need for resources.

Throughout its work the Steering Group recognised that judgement must continue to play a part in reaching conclusions about fairness in the allocation of resources. However, evidence about the influence of the age and sex structure of the population, morbidity and life circumstances, and remoteness on the relative need for healthcare resources has been used to inform these judgements. The increased use of evidence in this work represents a significant advance over the current SHARE formula.

5.   Some of the comments received during consultation expressed concern about the lack of transparency in the methods and results in *Fair Shares for All.* This concern applied especially to the methods used to assess the influence of morbidity and life circumstances on the relative needs of different population groups for healthcare. The Steering Group has sought to simplify the methods and improve the transparency of the proposed formula.

6.   This Review has turned a new page in the work related to resource allocation in the NHS, but it is certainly not the last page. The Steering Group recognises that additional work will be required over the next few years to develop further the evidence base. There are some areas where the data need to be improved, though this will take a few years, and no doubt there will be scope for developing and refining the methods of analysis used in this review. However the Steering Group is satisfied that this review has established a fair and evidence-based method of allocating resources between Health Boards

EXECUTIVE SUMMARY

1.   The Steering Group has considered carefully the comments received during consultation on *Fair Shares for All*, and a significant amount of additional work has been carried out to address the issues raised about the earlier proposals. This has involved a detailed and thorough review of the data, the methods of analysis and the results.

THE DATA

2.   During consultation some concerns were expressed about the quality of the data used to analyse the influence of different factors on the relative need for healthcare resources. All of the data used in this work have been carefully reviewed including the choice of population base, information on patient activity and costs, and indicators of morbidity and life circumstances. *Fair Shares for All* recognised the concerns about the limited range of statistics on community health services and general medical services. While there is certainly scope to improve the data in certain areas, **the Steering Group remains satisfied that the available data are suitable for the purposes for which they have been used, and that this information enables reliable conclusions to be drawn about how best to allocate resources to meet the needs of populations living in different Health Boards.** We are fortunate in the wide range and quality of data available to us in Scotland which is recognised to be among the best in the world.

STABILITY

3.   A key aspect of the further work that has been carried out in recent months has been a test of the stability of the proposed allocation formula, especially when applied to Health Boards with relatively small populations. This has been done by applying the analysis to data for another year, 1997-98. The earlier proposals were based on data for 1996-97; full data for 1997-98 were not available when that work was done. This additional work suggested that in certain care programmes the estimates of the relative need for healthcare resources in some Health Boards could change significantly from year-to-year. The approach has therefore been modified to take account of this, and the Steering Group is satisfied that **the revised formula outlined in this report is stable even when applied to Health Boards with relatively small populations.**

TRANSPARENCY

4.   Concern was expressed during consultation about the complexity of some aspects of the proposed formula, especially the method used to estimate the influence of morbidity and life circumstances on the need for healthcare. **The Steering Group recognises the importance of making the formula more transparent, and has sought to simplify the method by developing a single index (the 'Arbuthnott index') that captures the influence of the key aspects of morbidity and life circumstances on healthcare needs.** This retains the evidence-based approach of *Fair Shares for All* and provides a formula which remains responsive to the influence of morbidity and life circumstances on the need for

healthcare. It takes into account the influence of these circumstances on each care programme, and it will also be responsive to changes over time in the relative needs of the population living in different Health Board areas.

'ARBUTHNOTT INDEX'

5.   In *Fair Shares for All* a large number of different indicators (some 50 in total) were used to analyse the influence of morbidity and life circumstances on the relative need for healthcare. The further work that has been done suggests that there are a small number of key indicators that are closely associated with healthcare needs. These are:

- the mortality rate among people under 65;
- the unemployment rate;
- the proportion of elderly people on income support; and
- households with two or more indicators of deprivation.

6.   These four indicators have been combined into a single index, the 'Arbuthnott index', and this has been used to estimate the relationship between morbidity and life circumstances and the relative need for healthcare. Figure 1 shows the estimated level of this index in each Health Board area in 1996-97 and 1997-98.

- Health Boards where the index is greater than zero have levels of morbidity and deprivation that are above the national average. Greater Glasgow, for example, has the highest levels of morbidity and deprivation as measured by this index.
- Health Boards where the index is less than zero have levels of morbidity and deprivation that are below the national average.

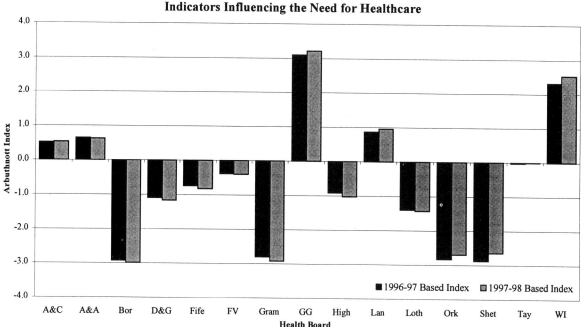

Figure 1: Arbuthnott Index, The Index of Morbidity and Life Circumstance Indicators Influencing the Need for Healthcare

4

7.   **The 'Arbuthnott index' is a measure of the morbidity and life circumstances that** *influence* **healthcare needs; it is not a** *direct measure* **of those needs.** However it can be used to estimate relative healthcare needs by examining the statistical relationship between the 'Arbuthnott index' and the use made of services by the population living in different areas of Scotland. Figure 2 provides two examples of the relationship between the 'Arbuthnott index' and the use of services for respiratory diseases and cancer. (The estimated relationships shown in this chart are based on statistical evidence.)

- The evidence shows that in areas of the country where the 'Arbuthnott index' has a relatively high value, greater use is made of health services for the treatment of both respiratory diseases and cancer. The populations living in areas of deprivation suffer from relatively high levels of respiratory diseases and cancer and this is reflected in increased use of health services.

- The evidence in Figure 2 also shows that the extent to which the 'Arbuthnott index' is associated with increased use of healthcare is not the same across all diseases. Deprivation has a much stronger influence on the need for services for respiratory diseases than it has on the need for services for cancer.

Figure 2: Relationship Between the Use of Services for Respiratory Diseases and Cancer and the Arbuthnott Index

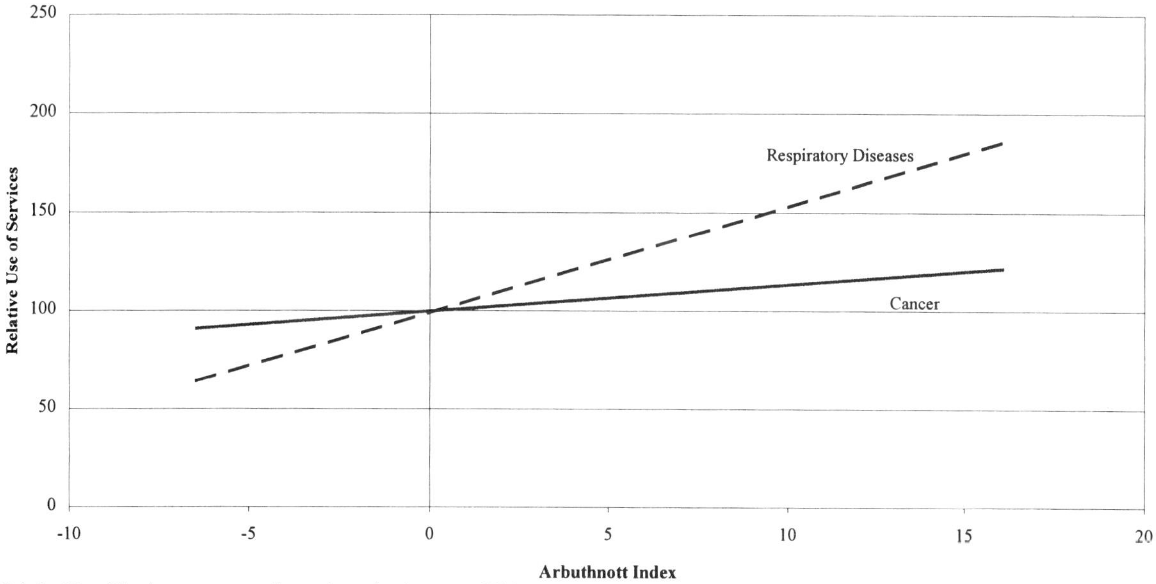

Relative Use of Services are expressed around a national average of 100
This illustration is based on all postcode sectors

This statistical analysis of the strength of the relationship between the 'Arbuthnott index' and the use of services in each care programme provides the evidence used to estimate the relative need for healthcare resources of the population living in each Health Board area. The stronger this relationship, the higher the proportion of resources that will need to be allocated to Boards with relatively high levels of deprivation.

8.   It is important that the 'Arbuthnott index' should also be responsive to changes over time in the underlying circumstances that influence healthcare needs. The 'Arbuthnott index' uses three indicators that can be updated each year (the mortality rate among people under 65, the unemployment rate, and the proportion of elderly people on income support). The inclusion of these three indicators will ensure that this index is responsive to changes in the

relative healthcare needs of the populations living in different Health Board areas. The fourth indicator (households with two or more indicators of deprivation) is taken from the 1991 census. Some concerns were expressed during consultation that census data may be out of date. However, the purpose of this review is to identify current relative needs for healthcare and these needs are influenced by past was well as present circumstances.

9.   The development of a single index to capture the influence of morbidity and life circumstances on relative needs for healthcare is the most important development in the further work that has been done in response to consultation. The Steering Group consider that this development has a number of important advantages.

- This approach continues to be evidence-based; a key requirement in developing a new formula. The selection of the indicators that make up the 'Arbuthnott index' is based on evidence, and the proposed formula is built up from statistical evidence about the strength of the relationship between this index and the need for healthcare in different care programmes and disease groups.
- The four indicators included in the 'Arbuthnott index' are generally recognised as closely linked with healthcare needs.
- The index is very stable as shown by the estimates for both 1996-97 and 1997-98.
- It represents a useful combination of indicators which can be updated each year as well as an indicator from the 1991 Census.
- Overall this approach has much greater transparency.

DEMOGRAPHY

10.   Some concerns were raised during consultation about the recommendation that the population shares used in the new formula should be based on the Mid-Year Estimates of Population produced by the General Register Office for Scotland (GROS) rather than the Population Projections also produced by GROS. The choice of population base is a key consideration because of its importance in the overall allocation formula, and the Steering Group has reviewed carefully this recommendation. Further work has been done to assess the relative accuracy of Mid-Year Estimates of Population and the Population Projections and **the evidence shows very clearly that the Mid-Year Estimates are significantly more reliable than the Population Projections as the basis for determining revenue allocations between Health Boards.**

11.   The earlier recommendation was influenced by advice from the General Register Office for Scotland who are the experts on population data in Scotland. They have confirmed that in their view the Mid-Year Estimates of Population are the most appropriate population figures to use in this instance, where the formula for allocating health service resources is based on the proportionate distribution of the population within Scotland.

12.   The method of estimating the influence of the age and sex structure of the population on the need for healthcare resources has also been reviewed, and the sensitivity of the results to alternative assumptions has been examined. On the basis of this additional work a number of refinements have been made to the earlier method of estimating the effects of population age and sex structure on healthcare needs.

REMOTENESS

13.   An important feature of the recommendations in *Fair Shares for All* was that an adjustment should be introduced to reflect the additional costs faced by some Health Boards in delivering services to populations living in remote and rural areas. This aspect of the proposed formula has also been reviewed. Two particular concerns raised during consultation were whether the proposed formula treated island communities in a consistent manner, and whether it took account of the mixed urban and rural areas of Boards such as Argyll and Clyde. A number of revisions have been made to the method of estimating the influence of remoteness on hospital costs.

GENERAL MEDICAL SERVICES (GMS)

14.   Because of the innovative nature of the formula proposed for GMS in *Fair Shares for All* this recommendation attracted a good deal of comment during consultation. A Working Group was set up to review the proposed GMS formula and provide advice to the Steering Group. A number of improvements have been made to this formula and on the basis of this review the Steering Group has concluded that:

- it is important that a formula should now be established for allocating GMS resources in place of the current allocation which largely reflects historical circumstances rather than more objective measures of need;
- although the data currently available on patient activity in GMS are limited, they provide a sufficient basis on which to estimate the relative needs of different population groups, and they highlight some anomalies in the current distribution of resources;
- efforts should be made to develop further the evidence base by improving the range and quality of data available on patient activity in GMS;
- a start should be made on applying a formula to GMS resources, though further consideration needs to be given to some of the practical issues about implementation of a resource allocation formula in this area.

The development of a formula for the allocation of GMS resources represents a very significant development in the allocation of healthcare resources in Scotland.

RESULTS

15.   Table 1 sets out the changes in each Health Board's share of Hospital and Community Health Services (HCHS) and GP prescribing resources as a result of the proposed formula compared with current share of these resources received by each Board in 2000-01. For example the figures show that Argyll and Clyde's share of these resources will fall from 8.62% to 8.47%, while Ayrshire and Arran's share will increase from 7.33% to 7.54%. Although the changes from the current allocation shares largely reflect the impact of the proposed formula, it should be noted that these changes are also influenced by other factors including changes in Health Board population shares. The SHARE formula which has been used to allocate resources between Health Boards over the last 20 years has effectively been frozen since 1997-98, and the current distribution of resources reflects the population figures used at that time. The proposed distribution of resources is based on the latest Mid-Year

Estimates of population, and for some Boards the changes in population shares in recent years is significant.

Table 1: Current (2000-01) and New Allocation Shares of Hospital and Community Services and GP Prescribing Resources

Health Board	Current (2000-01) Allocation Share %	New Allocation Share %	Change in Share %
Scotland	100.00	100.00	0.0
Argyll & Clyde	8.62	8.47	-1.7
Ayrshire & Arran	7.33	7.54	3.0
Borders	2.13	2.11	-1.0
Dumfries & Galloway	3.08	3.10	0.9
Fife	6.38	6.45	1.1
Forth Valley	5.13	5.12	-0.1
Grampian	9.50	9.08	-4.4
Greater Glasgow	19.10	19.61	2.7
Highland	4.12	4.42	7.2
Lanarkshire	10.34	10.43	0.9
Lothian	14.16	13.69	-3.3
Orkney	0.43	0.42	-2.3
Shetland	0.53	0.47	-10.1
Tayside	8.38	8.24	-1.7
Western Isles	0.79	0.84	6.0

Note: the current share is based on the unified budget allocations to Health Boards for Hospital and Community Health Services and GP prescribing in 2000-01. This share takes into account the special islands allowance allocated to the three island Health Boards, and excludes GMS cash limited and 'out of hours' services.

16. The implications of these changes for expenditure at Health Board level need to be treated with care. It is clear from the responses made to *Fair Shares for All* that it was widely assumed that a reduction in the **share of resources** received by a Health Board would mean a reduction in the **actual level of resources** received by that Board. **The Minister for Health and Community Care gave a clear assurance, however, that all Boards would receive real terms growth in resources during the lifetime of this Parliament.**

17. In practice, changes in the level of funds allocated to each Board for Hospital and Community Health Services and GP prescribing over the next few years will depend on a number of factors including:

- the overall increase in the level of expenditure on the NHS in Scotland, and the distribution of these funds between Hospital and Community Health Services and GP prescribing and other services;
- the minimum increase in funding that all Boards will receive;
- changes in population shares (Boards' allocations will be influenced by changes in their population shares as well as by the introduction of the recommended formula); and
- changes in other factors (e.g. the 'Arbuthnott index') that can influence the assessment of the relative need of each Health Board's population.

18. Changes in the formula used to assess relative needs is therefore only one factor that will influence the level of expenditure in each Health Board over the next few years. While it is not possible to forecast with certainty all of these factors, it is possible at this stage to

assess likely trends in expenditure in each Board over the next few years using the following assumptions.

- Total expenditure on Hospital and Community Health Services and GP prescribing in Scotland will increase by 5.5% per annum from 2001-02 onwards.
- Every Health Board will receive the increase in funding for these services of which they have already been notified in 2001-02. In 2002-03 and 2003-04 they will receive an increase in expenditure of at least 4% per annum.
- The difference between this minimum and the total increase in expenditure will be allocated to those Boards whose share of resources needs to increase whether because of changes in the allocation formula, changes in the distribution of the population or other factors. Thus progress towards the new allocation targets will be achieved through 'levelling up'.

19.   The estimates of the growth in the funds allocated to each Health Board between 2000-01 and 2003-04 using these assumptions are shown in Table 2. Note that the figures in this table show the projected increases in funding in real terms - i.e. after discounting the cash increases to reflect assumed inflation of 2.5% a year as measured by the GDP deflator. The final column of Table 2 shows the overall growth in resources that each Board will receive at constant 2000-01 prices between 2000-01 and 2003-04 based on these assumptions.

Table 2: Illustrative Allocations to Health Boards for HCHS and GP Prescribing at 2000-01 Prices

Health Board	2000-01 £m	2001-02 £m	2002-03 £m	2003-04 £m	Change 2000-01 to 2003-04 £m
Scotland	4,141.8	4,263.3	4,388.1	4,516.5	374.7
Argyll & Clyde	356.9	366.0	371.4	380.0	23.1
Ayrshire & Arran	303.5	314.2	327.8	339.1	35.6
Borders	88.3	90.6	92.9	96.0	7.7
Dumfries & Galloway	127.5	130.7	135.4	139.8	12.4
Fife	264.2	273.0	282.8	292.5	28.2
Forth Valley	212.4	217.2	224.1	231.9	19.5
Grampian	393.4	401.1	406.9	412.9	19.5
Greater Glasgow	790.9	820.5	851.9	879.1	88.3
Highland	170.8	179.0	191.8	200.1	29.3
Lanarkshire	428.1	441.7	456.3	471.5	43.4
Lothian	586.4	601.6	610.4	625.7	39.2
Orkney	17.8	18.4	18.6	19.0	1.1
Shetland	21.8	22.1	22.5	22.8	1.0
Tayside	347.0	353.3	359.4	369.2	22.2
Western Isles	32.7	34.0	35.8	37.0	4.2

Note: the money covers the unified budget allocations to Health Boards for Hospital and Community Health Services and GP prescribing in 2000-01. This share takes into account the special islands allowance allocated to the three island Health Boards, and excludes GMS cash limited and 'out of hours' services.

20.   In total the resources available for HCHS and GP prescribing would increase by £374.7m after allowing for inflation of 2.5% a year. All Health Boards would also receive growth in resources significantly in excess of this inflation rate. Figure 3 shows how expenditure per head of population on Hospital and Community Health Services and GP prescribing would increase in each Health Board over the next 3 years.

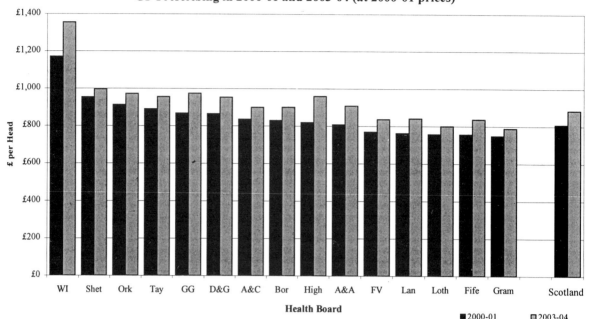

Figure 3: Expenditure per Head on Hospital and Community Health Services and GP Prescribing in 2000-01 and 2003-04 (at 2000-01 prices)

CONCLUSIONS

21.   This review of the resource allocation formula for the NHS in Scotland has taken two and a half years, including a very extensive and thorough consultation exercise. The Steering Group has looked carefully at the data used, the methods of analysis and the results, and a number of improvements have been made to the proposed formula to take account of the comments received during consultation. The Steering Group is satisfied that a sound basis has been established for adopting a resource allocation formula which in comparison with the current SHARE formula:

- is based on much better evidence;
- reflects more accurately the influence of morbidity and life circumstances on healthcare needs;
- takes into account more fully the influence of remoteness on the costs of delivering healthcare;
- will achieve a more equitable distribution of resources.

22.   At the same time the Steering Group recognises - as explained in *Fair Shares for All* - that there is a need to do further work in a number of key areas. In particular, there is a need to improve the range and quality of data available on community health services and general medical services, and more work should be done on the influence of remoteness on the costs of providing services. Nevertheless, the Steering Group considers that this work represents a substantial advance on the current SHARE formula, and strongly recommends that a start should now be made in implementing the proposed formula for Hospital and Community Health Services and GP Prescribing. A start should also be made to apply the formula for the allocation of resources for General Medical Services, though the Steering Group recognises that this is an area where further work needs to be done to improve the data and that some

consideration needs to be given to how changes in the distribution of resources for General Medical Services should be achieved.

CHAPTER 1:
RESPONSE TO COMMENTS ABOUT THE BASIC METHODS IN *FAIR SHARES FOR ALL*

1.1   A wide range of comments were received on *Fair Shares for All* during consultation, and some of these comments reflected concerns about the general approach that was adopted in the review. This chapter addresses some of these issues.

A) THE REMIT

1.2   The review was established in December 1997 with the following remit:

"To advise the Secretary of State for Scotland on methods for allocating the resources available to the National Health Service in Scotland, including both primary and secondary care, which are as objective and needs-based as available data and techniques permit with the aim of promoting equitable access to healthcare, and to bring forward recommendations to Ministers by June 1999."

Some of the comments on *Fair Shares for All* suggested that this remit was too narrow and that the Review should have encompassed wider issues about the overall level of funding of the NHS and the relationship between the NHS and the services provided by local authorities and other agencies.

1.3   The remit for this review was set by Ministers and clearly the Steering Group had to work within these terms of reference. However, the Steering Group does not consider that the terms of reference were restrictive. Issues about the overall level of funding of the NHS and about the relationship between the NHS and other organisations are obviously important. However whatever level of funding is provided for the NHS, a fair method of distributing these funds between Health Boards is still required and this is the issue on which the Steering Group was asked to provide advice. It is also worth noting that in practical terms it would have been unrealistic to expect the Steering Group to address issues about the level of funding and relationships with other organisations as well as developing a new formula for allocating NHS resources.

B) A SINGLE FORMULA FOR ALL HEALTH BOARDS

1.4   Some have questioned whether it is feasible to develop a single resource allocation formula that can be applied to the widely differing circumstances of large mainland Health Boards, some of which have populations of over 500,000, and island Health Boards with populations of only 20,000 to 30,000. The Steering Group is satisfied that the factors that influence relative needs for healthcare are as relevant to populations living in island Boards as to larger mainland Boards. The issue concerns the extent to which the indicators of need that would be used in a formula may become less stable when calculated for relatively small populations.

1.5   Under the current SHARE formula, for example, the standardised mortality rate among people under the age of 65 (SMR0-64) is used as an indicator of relative need.

Although this indicator is based on data for the three latest years it can still fluctuate between one year and the next in areas with relatively small populations. To achieve a greater degree of stability the SHARE formula calculates an overall average mortality rate for the 3 island Heath Boards as a group. This indicator is then applied uniformly to each island Board's population. The advantage of this approach is that it smooths out some of the erratic movements in the SMR0-64, but the consequence is that some of the underlying differences between the 3 island Boards in their relative healthcare needs are ignored.

1.6   It is important that the allocation of resources to each Health Board, including the island Boards, should reflect as far as possible the particular healthcare needs of its population. The levels of morbidity and deprivation in the Western Isles, for example, are considerably higher than in Shetland and Orkney and this should be taken into account in the formula. At the same time it is important to recognise the concerns that have been raised about the stability of the proposed formula, especially when applied to relatively small populations. To test the stability of the models the analysis has been applied to data for two years and, where necessary, adjustments have been made to the methods to improve stability. **On the basis of the evidence outlined later in this report the Steering Group has concluded that the proposed formula is stable when applied to the island Boards.**

C) ANALYSIS AT CARE PROGRAMME LEVEL

1.7   A number of issues were raised about the structure of care programmes used in the review. The main concerns were:

- the compartmentalisation of funding for care programmes weakens the incentives for integrated finance and delivery of services spanning different institutional and care settings;
- the expenditure shares calculated for each Health Board by care programme may be seen as inflexible targets which do not take account of differing patterns of care between Boards;

COMPARTMENTALISATION OF FUNDING

1.8   The 8 care programmes used in the review were:

- acute hospital services
- mental illness hospital services
- care of the elderly hospital services
- maternity hospital services
- specialist hospital services for patients with learning disabilities
- community health services
- GP prescribing
- general medical services

1.9   The Steering Group does not consider that the method of estimating relative healthcare needs separately for each of these care programmes weakens the incentives for Health Boards to provide integrated services. **Although separate care programmes are** used to analyse relative needs, this does not mean that separate ('compartmentalised') funding is provided for each care programme. Health Boards receive a single allocation that covers Hospital and Community Health Services and GP prescribing, and it is for Boards to determine how these funds should be allocated between different forms of care.

1.10   It is also worth noting that the care programmes used in the review are not very different from the care programmes that have been used in the current SHARE formula for the last 20 or so years.   It has not been suggested that progress in transferring care from hospital into the community in recent years has been inhibited by the use of these different care programmes in the SHARE formula.

EXPENDITURE SHARES MAY BECOME INFLEXIBLE TARGETS

1.11   Although the analysis identifies each Health Board's relative need for resources within the different care programmes, these estimates should not be seen as expenditure 'targets'. Health Boards may wish to compare their actual expenditure on particular care programmes with the estimates that are used in calculating their relative need for resources. Indeed, they can do this with the estimates that are currently made for different care programmes in the SHARE formula. However such estimates need to be treated with caution. They are a means of estimating the relative need for healthcare resources in different Health Board areas, but they are not intended to be used as targets which effectively prescribe how Health Boards should spend these resources on different forms of care.

D) THE USE OF EVIDENCE BASED ON RECENT PATTERNS OF CARE

1.12   Some Health Boards were concerned that by relying on recent evidence about the use made of services in assessing relative needs, the proposed formula may discriminate against those Boards that have made significant changes in the pattern of services provided for their populations. For example, Boards that have made considerable progress in shifting the pattern of care from hospital into the community thought that estimates of relative need based on an analysis of the use of mental illness hospital services would conclude that their relative need for resources is small because they have relatively few patients in hospital. If this was how the estimates of relative need were arrived at then clearly it could provide a disincentive to develop community care.

1.13   The allocation of resources under the proposed formula is not, in fact, based on each Board's **actual** pattern of services. It is based on evidence drawn from **national data** about the influence of the age and sex structure of the population and the influence of morbidity and life circumstances on healthcare needs. For example, the adjustment for morbidity and life circumstances is estimated using the following approach.

- Information about patterns of care and treatment across Scotland as a whole is used to identify the relationship between the use made of services and the morbidity and deprivation characteristics of the population. This provides evidence about the extent to which, on average, people in deprived areas make greater use of services than people in more affluent areas.

- The observed use of services may also be influenced by the accessibility of services and by the policies adopted in different Health Board areas. (For example, some Boards may, for historic reasons, spend a higher proportion of their resources on a particular care programme than other Boards.) Statistically these other factors are controlled for in the analytical work. The issue that the analysis addresses therefore is this: **after taking account of differences in accessibility and differences between Health Boards in patterns of care, what relationship is there between the use made of services and indicators of need? Is there clear evidence that people from relatively deprived areas make greater use of services than people from more affluent areas?**
- The indicators of need that are used in this analysis reflect the different characteristics of the population in each area - for example, the proportion of people unemployed, or the proportion of people over 65 living on income support.
- The method of taking accessibility of services into account in this analysis has been improved in response to concerns that were raised during consultation.

1.14   It is this analysis of the relationship across Scotland as a whole between the use of services and deprivation that influences the allocation of resources between Health Boards. **The share of resources that a particular Board is estimated to need is determined solely by the characteristics of its population - for example the extent to which is has a relatively high proportion of elderly people or a relatively high proportion living in deprived circumstances. The allocation of resources is not influenced by *how* a Board chooses to deliver services to its population.** Therefore Boards that have transferred a relatively high proportion of care from hospital into the community are not in any way disadvantaged in the proposed formula.

E) THE USE OF SMALL AREA DATA

1.15   The analysis of the relationship between the use of services and indicators of need is based on data collected at small area level - i.e. postcode sector level. On average each of the postcode sectors used in the analysis in *Fair Shares for All* had a population of around 5,000 people, though this number can vary significantly. During consultation it was suggested that analysis of small area data might be distorted by the inclusion of postcode sectors with very small populations. This issue has been reviewed and very small postcode sectors have been amalgamated to reduce the risk that the results of the analysis could be affected by small numbers. The average size of population in the postcode sectors is now 7,000, and only 3 sectors have a population of less than 1,000 people. Further statistical tests were carried out on this data to ensure that the results were not distorted by differences in population between postcode sectors.

1.16   Some of the comments received during consultation also questioned whether sound conclusions could be drawn from an analysis at small area level because of the heterogeneous socio-economic character of many postcode sectors. The heterogeneous character of postcode sectors is not a disadvantage given the purpose for which the small area data is being used - i.e. to identify how deprivation influences the need for healthcare resources. By comparing postcode sectors with varying levels of deprivation it is possible to measure how the use of services changes as the indicators of morbidity and deprivation change. For example, this information shows how the use made of acute hospital services changes as the average level of unemployment in an area varies, and it therefore enables estimates to be made of the extent to which Health Boards with relatively high levels of unemployment require additional resources because of the greater healthcare needs of their populations.

1.17   It would be quite a different matter if this information were to be used to determine how resources should actually be targeted on the most deprived **individuals** in the population. Information about the *average* level of deprivation in postcode sectors could not be used for this purpose since this average could conceal pockets of severe deprivation.

F) QUALITY OF DATA

1.18   Some concerns were expressed during consultation about the quality of the data. The review drew on a wide range of data including health service statistics on patient activity and costs, population data provided by the Registrar General for Scotland, morbidity and mortality data, and information from the 1991 census about the socio-economic characteristics of small areas. As explained in *Fair Shares for All* there are some areas - in particular community health services and general medical services - where the available data are limited. However, the weaknesses of the data need to be kept in perspective. **Much of the data is of good quality and considerable efforts are made by the organisations responsible for the different datasets to maintain and improve quality. These statistics are also widely used in the health services for clinical and management purposes and for research.**

1.19   There are a number of areas where some revisions have been made to the data used in the analysis. For example, the sensitivity of estimates of the costs of services used by each age and sex group in the population was examined by exploring a number of different methods of costing the use of services. Although the results showed that the alternative methods produced very similar results, a number of refinements were made to the method. Other areas where some improvements have been made to take account of concerns about data quality include community health services and general medical services.

G) RANGE OF SERVICES COVERED IN THE REVIEW

1.20   Some concerns were expressed that the review did not cover certain services, in particular:

- the role of specialist centres;
- the wider health promotion and prevention role of Health Boards;
- general dental services, general ophthalmic services, and other areas of Family Health Services.

SPECIALIST CENTRES

1.21   It has been suggested that the review did not take into account the particular problems faced by teaching Health Boards whose local Trusts provide specialist services to the population of neighbouring Health Boards as well as to their own population. The Steering Group is very conscious of the important role of specialist services in the NHS but a resource allocation formula does not require a specific adjustment to take account of these services.

- In the first place the purpose of this review is to ensure that the distribution of resources between Health Boards reflects **the relative healthcare needs of their populations**, and to some extent the population of every Health Board will make use of services in specialist centres. Health Boards that send patients to be treated by specialist services in a teaching Board will provide payments to the teaching hospitals for that service. Some teaching hospitals and their Boards argue that they are not fully reimbursed by other Boards for these specialist services, but that is not a matter for a resource allocation formula. It is an issue to be sorted out between the specialist centres and the Boards concerned.

- Second, some of the additional costs in specialist centres are associated with their responsibilities for teaching medical students. These costs are funded separately through an allocation that is intended to cover the Additional Costs of Teaching (ACT). **The money distributed for ACT is not affected by the proposed formula for allocating the resources that Health Boards use to provide services for patients**.

CARE PROGRAMMES ARE FOCUSED ON CARE AND TREATMENT

1.22   A criticism made of the approach adopted in the review is that the care programmes concentrate on the care and treatment of patients and do not reflect the wider responsibilities of Health Boards to promote good health and prevent illness. These care programmes account for the overwhelming proportion of Health Board expenditure. Total expenditure on health promotion and prevention accounts for a relatively small, though important, proportion of total expenditure compared with expenditure on, say, acute hospital services or mental illness services. Inevitably the review concentrated on developing separate models for those areas which cover the main services provided through Health Boards.

1.23   This does not mean that health promotion and prevention have been ignored. Under the proposed formula the resources that are spent on these services would be allocated between Boards in the same way as resources for community health services. Therefore Health Boards with high levels of deprivation would receive a relatively high share of health promotion and prevention resources. It is also worth emphasising again that the proposed formula, though developed through the analysis of care programmes, is not prescriptive about how Health Boards should spend their resources. It is for Boards to determine whether they should increase the proportion of their resources spent on health promotion and prevention.

FAMILY HEALTH SERVICES

1.24   The review covered most of the services for which money is distributed to Health Boards. However several allocations relating to Family Health Services (such as general dental services and general ophthalmic services) were not included in the review. This simply reflected a practical decision that it was not possible to cover all of these services in the timescale set for the review. However it is important that these other areas should also be examined in future work.

H) INCENTIVES FOR HEALTH BOARDS

1.25   In several comments a concern was expressed that the proposed allocation formula does not provide financial incentives for Health Boards to improve the health of their populations, and that in some respects it might actually create perverse incentives. The proposed formula uses several indicators including the mortality rate among people under 65 and, to the extent that a Board is relatively successful at improving the health of its population and reducing mortality, this will mean that its share of resources may fall. The Steering Group considers that in practice it is extremely unlikely that the proposed formula would discourage Health Boards from adopting policies that improve the health of their populations. Again it is worth noting that the same concern could be raised about the current SHARE formula which uses the mortality rate among people under 65 as an indicator of relative need. There is no evidence to suggest that the use of this indicator has discouraged Health Boards from seeking to improve health. In this context it is also worth noting that the effects of any new formula should be monitored carefully so that concerns can be addressed.

I) THE ADJUSTMENT FOR REMOTENESS

1.26   The proposed adjustment for remoteness attracted a considerable number of comments during consultation. It was widely accepted that some adjustment is required in the formula to take account of the additional costs of providing hospital and community services in remote and rural areas. However some concerns were raised about the treatment of island communities and Health Boards with a mixture of urban and rural areas. The Steering Group has reviewed these particular issues carefully and has addressed them in the further work that has been done.

1.27   A more general concern expressed about the remoteness adjustment is that this may simply reimburse some hospitals that have high costs because they are relatively inefficient and as a result it may create a perverse incentive to keep costs high in small hospitals in remote and rural areas. There are several points to note here. First, the proposed adjustment does not reimburse Health Boards in remote and rural areas for their *actual* costs. This would obviously remove any incentive to control costs. **The proposed adjustment would reflect the extent to which *on average* Health Boards in remote and rural areas are estimated to face relatively high costs, and it would be based on objective indicators of remoteness.** Second, this method should not weaken the incentive for Health Boards and hospitals in remote and rural areas to run hospitals efficiently and keep costs under control. Any savings which an individual hospital and Health Board achieve through greater efficiency would not be offset by a change in their allocation through the formula.

J) ANOMALIES BETWEEN HEALTH BOARDS

1.28   Some of the comments received drew attention to apparent anomalies between Health Boards in the results set out in *Fair Shares for All*. The particular examples raised are discussed in subsequent chapters. It is worth emphasising here, however, that *apparent* anomalies may well be explained by differences between Health Boards in the factors that influence the relative needs of their populations for healthcare. For example, it was thought surprising that the formula should propose different overall adjustments for the island Health

Boards. However some of the key factors that influence healthcare needs such as the age and sex structure of the population and levels of deprivation differ significantly among these 3 Boards. A particular anomaly that was raised during consultation was the substantial difference in the estimated effect of remoteness on the costs of providing general medical services in Borders compared with Dumfries and Galloway. This anomaly has been resolved in the further work.

K) SCALE OF REDISTRIBUTION

1.29   Some of the comments suggested that the scale of redistribution of resources that would take place under the proposed formula compared with the current allocation was disappointingly small. In fact the scale of change in allocation shares under the revised proposals range from a reduction of 10.1% in Shetland to an increase of 7.2% in Highland. These are very significant changes. It should also be borne in mind that these are from a current allocation formula that already takes some account of morbidity and deprivation through the use of the standardised mortality rate among people under 65 as an indicator of need in the formula for non-obstetric and non-psychiatric services. The proposed formula shows much larger changes if compared against a baseline in which every Health Board was given the same allocation per head of population.

1.30   In the end what matters is whether a sound formula has been established that reflects the influence of different factors on the relative need for healthcare. Having considered the available evidence the Steering Group is satisfied that the proposed formula provides a much more effective means of taking all of these factors into account than the present formula.

L) THE COMPLEXITY OF THE FORMULA

1.31   Some concerns were expressed during consultation about the complexity of the methods used in developing a new formula and the difficulties this posed for understanding by health service staff and the wider public. This concern was raised mainly in relation to the adjustment proposed for morbidity and life circumstances. To develop an evidence base for adjusting the allocation of resources to take account of morbidity and life circumstances inevitably requires quite complex methods of analysis. However the Steering Group has considerably revised the approach by developing a single index (the 'Arbuthnott index') that captures the key aspects of the morbidity and life circumstances that influence healthcare needs. This approach has a number of advantages including:

- it remains an evidence-based method of assessing the influence of morbidity and life circumstances on healthcare needs;
- it provides results which are more consistent across care programmes than the earlier approach;
- the index is relatively simply to calculate and use.

CHAPTER 2:
POPULATION ESTIMATES AND ADJUSTMENTS FOR AGE AND SEX

2.1   This chapter considers some of the issues raised during consultation about:

- the estimates of the population share in each Health Board; and
- the adjustment to take account of the influence of the population's age and sex characteristics on healthcare needs.

POPULATION

2.2   The estimate of each Health Board's share of the total Scottish population is a key factor in a formula for allocating NHS resources. The current SHARE formula uses Population Projections produced by the General Register Office for Scotland (GROS) to calculate Health Board population shares. However, *Fair Shares for All* recommended that in future the formula should use the Mid-Year Estimates of Population - also produced by GROS - rather than the Population Projections. During consultation a number of issues were raised about this recommendation.

- It was suggested that Population Projections may be better than Mid-Year Estimates because the Projections should take account of most recent population shifts, whereas the Mid-Year Estimates are always slightly out of date.
- It was felt that the Community Health Index may provide a more appropriate measure of Health Board populations.
- Some concerns were expressed about the extent to which the proposed population measure takes account of temporary residents in each Health Board area - for example tourists who may make use of health services.

MID-YEAR ESTIMATES VERSUS POPULATION PROJECTIONS

2.3   *Fair Shares for All* explained that the Mid-Year Estimates of Health Board populations will lag slightly behind the year to which they are applied in the resource allocation formula. For example, decisions about the allocation of resources for 2001-02 have to be taken in the autumn of 2000 and at that point the latest available Mid-Year Estimate will be for mid-year 1999. The population figures will therefore lag 2 years behind the allocation year and will not take account of more recent shifts in the distribution of the population between Health Board areas.

2.4   However, although Population Projections may appear to have the advantage of being more up-to-date than Mid-Year Estimates, it is important to note that the Projections also have some disadvantages. They are derived from assumptions based on past trends in fertility, mortality and migration, and are therefore subject to a margin of error. They are not forecasts; they are simply the results of what would happen if the assumptions are actually realised. A change in the magnitude or the direction of the trend will significantly affect the projected population. As they are based on the Mid-Year Estimates, any uncertainties in those will be carried forward into the Projections. The Mid-Year Estimates are produced annually and therefore have the opportunity for improvement each year, whereas the Projections are generally updated every two years, so for one year out of every two the most up to date information on population will not be used.

2.5   In response to the concerns raised during consultation the Steering Group has done further work to compare the accuracy of the Mid-Year Estimates and the Population Projections in the context of revenue allocations using data for the previous 6 years. The comparison is based on the following method.

(a) The best available estimate of the population in any year is the Mid-Year Estimate for that year, once it becomes available.

(b) This estimate was compared against the two alternative figures that could have been used in an allocation formula (see table 2.1):
-   the Mid-Year Estimate of 2 years earlier; and
-   the Population Projection.

Table 2.1: Availability of Mid-Year Estimates and Projected Populations at the Time of Allocation

Date Allocation Calculated	Financial Year of Allocation	Available Mid-Year Estimate Population	Available Population Projection Base Year	Year of Projection
Oct-93	1994-95	1992	1989	1994
Oct-94	1995-96	1993	1989	1995
Oct-95	1996-97	1994	1992	1996
Oct-96	1997-98	1995	1992	1997
Oct-97	1998-99	1996	1994	1998
Oct-98	1999-00	1997	1996	1999
Oct-99	2000-01	1998	1996	2000

For example, in deciding on the allocation of resources for 1996-97 the latest available Mid-Year Estimate would have been 1994. The latest available Population Projection for 1996 that could have been used in allocating resources for 1996-97 would have been based on 1992 population data. These two figures were then compared against the actual Mid-Year Estimate for 1996 (which did not become available until 1997).

2.6   **The detailed results of this comparison which are outlined in Annex C show that the Mid-Year Estimates tend to be significantly more reliable than the Population Projections**. In 14 out of the 15 Health Boards the Mid-Year Estimates were more accurate and for the other Board the results were identical. The results also show that because the Population Projections are re-based every other year they provide an inherently less stable series over time than the Mid-Year Estimates – which essentially roll the population count forward by adding births, subtracting deaths and allowing for migration.[1]

2.7   These results confirm the recommendation in *Fair Shares for All* that it would be better to use Mid-Year Estimates rather than Population Projections in a new resource allocation formula. It is also worth noting that this recommendation was based on advice from the General Register for Scotland who are the experts on population data in Scotland. GROS have confirmed that in their view the Mid-Year Estimates will always provide a better reflection of the true population distribution within Scotland.

---

1 It is worth emphasising that this does not imply that the population projections produced by the General Register Office for Scotland are unreliable. It is a question of fitness for purpose. These projections are intended for medium and longer-term use in trend analysis and are not intended as absolute forecasts of short term population distributions and structures.

2.8   In carrying out this further work the opportunity has been taken to update the Mid-Year Population estimates. *Fair Shares for All* used the Mid-Year Estimates for 1996; this final report uses the Mid-Year Estimates for 1998 which are the latest that would have been available for determining the 2000-01 allocations.

2.9   The current SHARE formula was effectively frozen in 1997-98 pending the outcome of this review of resource allocation. At that point the Health Board population shares were Population Projections. As a result of freezing the SHARE formula significant, and growing, discrepancies have arisen between the population data that were used when SHARE was frozen and the latest 1998 Mid-Year Estimates that would be incorporated into a new formula. Table 2.2 shows the extent of these discrepancies.

Table 2.2: Population Figures in SHARE and Mid-Year Estimates of Population for 1998

Health Board	SHARE Population[1] % of total	Arbuthnott Population[2] % of total	Percentage Difference %
Scotland	100.00	100.00	0.0
Argyll & Clyde	8.36	8.34	-0.2
Ayrshire & Arran	7.35	7.33	-0.2
Borders	2.07	2.08	0.1
Dumfries & Galloway	2.89	2.88	-0.4
Fife	6.90	6.81	-1.2
Forth Valley	5.34	5.39	0.8
Grampian	10.52	10.26	-2.5
Greater Glasgow	17.54	17.80	1.5
Highland	4.10	4.07	-0.8
Lanarkshire	10.90	10.95	0.5
Lothian	14.89	15.11	1.5
Orkney	0.39	0.38	-2.7
Shetland	0.45	0.45	-1.3
Tayside	7.73	7.61	-1.5
Western Isles	0.57	0.55	-3.5

Note: 1) Latest SHARE formula froze population to 1997 projections (1992 based) (GROS)
2) Arbuthnott Formula uses the 1998 Mid-Year Estimate data (GROS)

2.10   Some of the changes shown in Table 2.2 are very significant. For example, Grampian's population share in the 1997-98 SHARE formula was 10.52%. This share has fallen to 10.26% based on the latest 1998 Mid-Year Estimates, a reduction of 2.5%. In contrast the population shares of Greater Glasgow and Lothian have each increased by 1.5%. These changes will affect the differences between Health Boards' *current* allocations and the allocations based on the revised formula in this report. Part of the difference reflects the use of the 1998 Mid-Year Estimates of Population rather than the out-of-date Population Projections in the frozen SHARE formula.

COMMUNITY HEALTH INDEX

2.11   The Community Health Index (CHI) is a record of all patients registered on Scottish GP lists and is based on regional records maintained by Health Boards. *Fair Shares for All* noted that the CHI has some attractions as a population estimate in a resource allocation formula since it is based on health service users. However, a weakness of the CHI at present is the problem of 'list size inflation' which is largely caused by delays in removing patients from GP lists who have left the area or died.

2.12 **The Steering Group now considers that there would be advantages in adopting the CHI as the population measure in the allocation formula for General Medical Services, despite the problem of list size inflation**. The reason for this is that payments to General Practitioners are based on the CHI population and it would be inconsistent to use a different measure of population in an allocation formula for General Medical Services. The Steering Group has therefore concluded that while the Mid-Year Estimates produced by GROS should be used in the allocation formula for Hospital and Community Health Services and for GP prescribing, the CHI population estimates should be used in any formula applied to General Medical Services. Current action to improve the quality of the CHI should lead in time to a much more even link between it and the Mid-Year Estimates of Population. Therefore, improvements to CHI coupled with progressive implementation of a new formula for GMS will bring GMS into alignment with HCHS and GP prescribing.

TEMPORARY RESIDENTS

2.13 While the permanent resident population in each Health Board area may account for the major part of the demands placed on health services, these demands are also influenced by temporary residents. There are two groups to note in particular: students and visitors. The population estimates produced by GROS estimate the resident population of Scotland and students are treated as being resident at their term time address. In GP prescribing and General Medical Services adjustments are made to the population data to take account of the additional demands associated with temporary residents.

ADJUSTMENT FOR POPULATION AGE AND SEX

2.14 The population of Health Boards differ in their age and sex characteristics and this has a significant effect on their relative need for healthcare resources. *Fair Shares for All* proposed a new method of estimating the weightings that should be applied to allow for age and sex differences between Health Board populations. This method takes into account:

- the use made of different specialties by each age/sex group;
- differences in the lengths of stay - elderly people tend to have longer lengths of stay than younger population groups;
- the costs of treatment and the way in which these costs are affected by length of stay.

2.15 A number of technical issues were raised during consultation about this method. Some Health Boards were concerned that estimates of the use of services based on patient activity data might be distorted by differences between Boards in patterns of care, especially in the acute sector. Some concerns were also expressed about the method of taking into account the effect of differences in lengths of stay on the costs of treating patients in different age groups. These issues are discussed in more detail in Annex D.

2.16 In response to these concerns the Steering Group has reviewed the method of calculating age/sex weights and has also examined the sensitivity of the results to alternative assumptions about the effects of lengths of stay on the costs of treating patients. A number of improvements have been made to these methods and Figure 2.1 shows the revised estimate of relative need for healthcare resources in each Health Board as a result of the age and sex structure of its population, and how the revised estimates compare with those published in *Fair Shares for All*. The revised estimates are very similar to the earlier estimates.

Figure 2.1: Relative Need For Resources Compared to National Average: Adjustment for Age and Sex

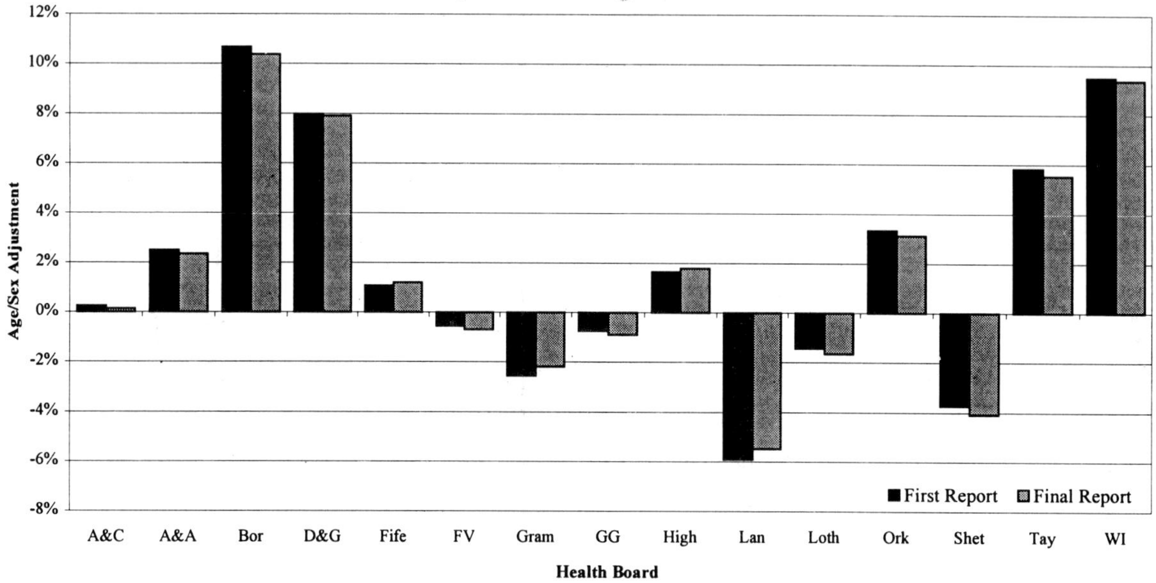

The First Report was based on models using data for 1996-97, the Final Report uses 1997-98 data
These adjustments are around a national adjustment of zero

CHAPTER 3:
MORBIDITY AND LIFE CIRCUMSTANCES

3.1 *Fair Shares for All* recommended that an adjustment should be included in the resource allocation formula to take account of the influence of morbidity and life circumstances on the need for healthcare. An evidence base for this adjustment was developed through statistical analysis at small area level of the relationship between a wide range of indicators of morbidity and life circumstances and the use made of different health services.

- In total there were about 50 different indicators of socio-economic circumstances including, for example, elderly people living alone, children in lone parent families, housing circumstances, unemployment, people living on income support, self reported sickness rates, and mortality rates.
- These indicators were calculated for small area (postcode sector) populations. There were almost 900 postcode sectors with an average population of around 5,700 people.
- Data were also collected on the actual use of different health services by the population in each postcode sector and this was compared with the expected use of these services (based on national averages).
- Statistical analysis was then used to estimate the relationship between these indicators and the use made of different healthcare services.
- The analysis took into account the effects of the accessibility of services on their use as well as differences in the pattern of services between Health Board areas. These factors are controlled for in the statistical analysis to ensure that they do not distort the relationship between the use of services and indicators of morbidity and life circumstances.

3.2 The main issues raised during consultation about this aspect of the proposed formula were as follows.

(a) There was a general concern that the methods lacked transparency and that the complex statistical analysis was difficult to understand.
(b) The models on which the proposed formula was based were developed using data for 1996-97. It was felt that they should be tested on data for another year to assess their stability.
(c) Although the average population in each postcode sector used in the analysis in *Fair Shares for All* was around 5,700, this figure varies and some postcode sectors had less than a few hundred people. There was concern that in postcode sectors with a small population the data on the use of services and the indicators of morbidity and life circumstances might take extreme values and distort the results of the analysis.
(d) The method used to assess the accessibility of services was questioned.
(e) Many of the socio-economic indicators were drawn from the 1991 census and it was felt that these figures might be out of date.

3.3 The Steering Group has carried out a thorough review of the methods used to assess the influence of morbidity and life circumstances on the relative need for healthcare resources in response to the comments provided during consultation, and the more technical aspects of this review are described in Annex E. Three considerations in particular have influenced this further work.

- First, the need to examine the stability of the models used to estimate the healthcare needs of different populations.
- Second, the need to achieve greater transparency in the methods of analysing the influence of morbidity and life circumstances on healthcare needs.
- Third the need to retain the sensitivity of the model to reflect the needs of differing population groups and to be responsive to changing circumstances.

3.4   To test the stability of the models, estimates of the effects of morbidity and life circumstances on healthcare needs were made using data for two years separately, 1996-97 and 1997-98. At the time of the earlier work full data for 1997-98 were not yet available. While the approach adopted in *Fair Shares for All* showed a broad measure of stability when applied to data for another year, the results for some care programmes and for some Health Boards differed significantly from one year to another. Detailed analysis of this issue suggested that the lack of stability was caused by the inclusion of a very large number of indicators of socio-economic circumstances in the analysis. The indicators that were identified as statistically significant sometimes differed from year to year, and this could affect the resulting estimates of relative need.

3.5   In reviewing the comments made during consultation about the analysis of morbidity and life circumstances the Steering Group has also been very conscious of the need to achieve greater transparency in this aspect of the proposed formula. The methods used in *Fair Shares for All* to analyse this issue were complex, and to some extent this is inevitable given the need to establish an evidence base for this adjustment. However, the Steering Group has considered how this approach could be simplified to improve its transparency.

AN ALTERNATIVE APPROACH

3.6   A number of options were examined for improving the treatment of morbidity and life circumstances in the proposed formula, and the Steering Group concluded that the most effective method of doing this was to develop a single index of morbidity and life circumstances. The analytical work provided evidence that there are a small number of key indicators that are closely associated with the use of health services, and these indicators have been combined into a single index of the factors that influence the need for healthcare. The four indicators selected on this basis are:

- the standardised mortality rate among people under the age of 65;
- the unemployment rate;
- the proportion of elderly people claiming income support; and
- households with two or more indicators of deprivation.

The following sections describe each of these indicators and the overall index into which they have been combined.

MORTALITY RATES AMONG PEOPLE UNDER 65

3.7   This is a well-established indicator of the need for healthcare which is used in the current SHARE formula, though it is only applied to non-psychiatric and non-obstetric services and to day and outpatient services by people under the age of 65. It is a good indicator of relative healthcare needs because areas with a relatively high mortality rate among people under 65 have populations that suffer from a wide range of health problems. Figure 3.1 shows how this indicator differs between Health Boards. For example, in Greater Glasgow - an area with very high levels of deprivation - the mortality rate among people under the age of 65 is almost 40% above the national average. In contrast, the mortality rate among people under the age of 65 in Grampian is 20% below the national average.

Figure 3.1: Standardised Mortality Rate Among People Aged Under 65 (1993-97)
(Scotland =100)

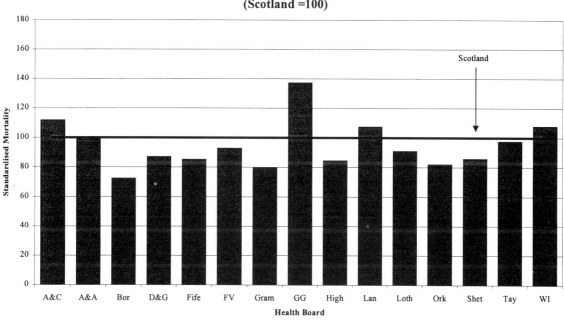

3.8   The usefulness of this indicator at small area level has sometimes been questioned on the grounds that a relatively small proportion of deaths occur among people aged under 65 and this proportion is falling as life expectancy improves. To address this issue the mortality rate among people under 65 has been calculated by taking an average over a 5 year period.

3.9   Other mortality rates were considered including the mortality rate among people under 75 and the mortality rate for all ages. However the evidence showed that the mortality rate among people under 65 is a more significant indicator than the alternative mortality rates. This may seem surprising since the alternative mortality rates span a wider age range. However, it is important to recognise that these are *indicators* that influence healthcare needs; they are not *direct measures* of these needs. **The mortality rate among people under 65 appears to be a good indicator of differences in healthcare needs generally among the population of all ages.**

STANDARDISED UNEMPLOYMENT RATES

3.10   This indicator measures the proportion of the population of working age who are claiming unemployment benefit. Unemployment is closely linked with deprivation and therefore this provides a general indicator of socio-economic circumstances that influence the need for healthcare. While unemployment rates change over time with the general level of economic activity in the economy, the *relative* level of unemployment in different areas of the country will remain comparatively stable. Figure 3.2 shows how this indicator varied between Health Boards in 1997-98 compared with a national average of 100.

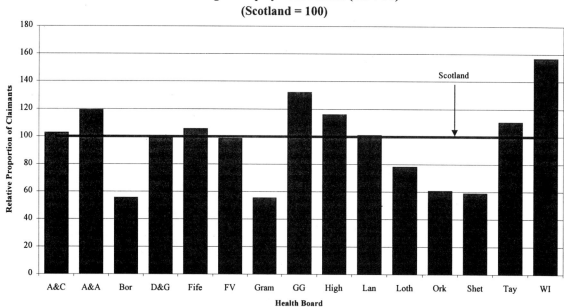

Figure 3.2: Relative Proportion of Population of Working Age
Claiming Unemployment Benefit (1997-98)
(Scotland = 100)

ELDERLY PEOPLE ON INCOME SUPPORT

3.11   This indicator measures the proportion of the population over the age of 65 claiming income support. The elderly account for a high proportion of the use made of different health services. However, it would be misleading to see this as an indicator that directly reflects the healthcare needs of the elderly. Areas of the country with a relatively high proportion of elderly people living on income support are likely to be areas with high levels of deprivation, and this will be reflected in increased healthcare needs in the population of all ages. Figure 3.3 shows the differences between Boards in the proportion of the elderly claiming income support compared with a national average of 100.

28

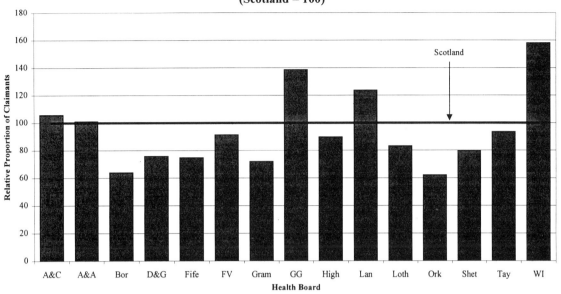

Figure 3.3: Standardised Proportion of Population Aged Over 65
Claiming Income Support (1997)
(Scotland = 100)

HOUSEHOLDS WITH TWO OR MORE INDICATORS OF DEPRIVATION

3.12   The Central Research Unit in the Scottish Executive derived measures of multiple deprivation in households using 1991 Census data. Six different indicators of deprivation were considered (unemployed or permanently sick head of household, low socio-economic group of head of household, overcrowding, large households, lone-parent family, and all-elderly household). Areas of Scotland with a relatively high proportion of households with multiple levels of deprivation will give rise to relatively high demands for healthcare. Figure 3.4 shows how this proportion varies between Health Boards compared with a national average of 100.

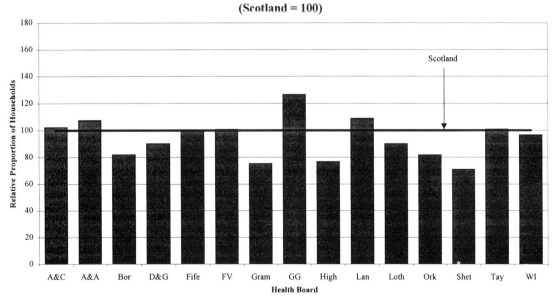

Figure 3.4: Relative Proportion of Households Having Two or More
Deprivation Indicators (1991 Census)
(Scotland = 100)

INDEX OF KEY INDICATORS (THE 'ARBUTHNOTT INDEX')

3.13   These four indicators have been combined into a single index in which they are given equal weight. The method of calculating this overall index is explained in Annex F. The values of this index range from -6.45 (the most affluent postcode sector in Scotland) to +16.06 (the most deprived postcode sector). Figure 3.5 shows the distribution of population within Scotland in relation to this index. Most of the population is distributed within relatively narrow range of the index. However the distribution is skewed to the right, indicating a small but significant proportion of the population living in very high levels of deprivation.

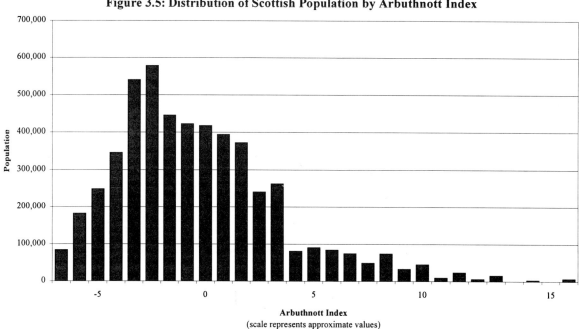

Figure 3.5: Distribution of Scottish Population by Arbuthnott Index

Arbuthnott Index
(scale represents approximate values)

The values of this index reflect areas of relative affluence and deprivation, from the most affluent areas (-ve) to the most deprived (+ve)

3.14   The average value of the 'Arbuthnott index' for each Health Board (Figure 3.6) reflects the distribution of its population between affluent and deprived areas. The range of this index is narrower at Health Board level (-3 to +3) than at postcode sector level because each Board has a mixture of relatively affluent and deprived areas. For example, although Greater Glasgow has a high proportion of the most deprived postcode sectors within Scotland it also has a significant number of relatively affluent areas. It is worth emphasising here that the estimates of the influence of this index on relative needs for healthcare are carried out for each postcode sector, and the results are aggregated to show the needs for the Health Board population as a whole.

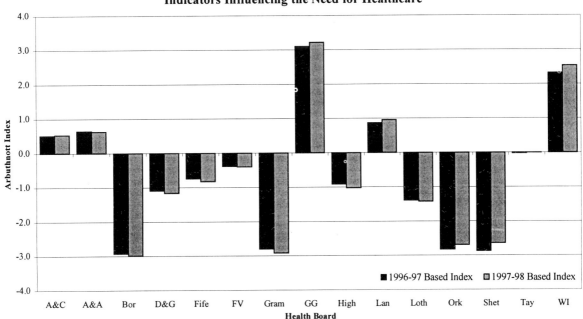

Figure 3.6: Arbuthnott Index, The Index of Morbidity and Life Circumstance Indicators Influencing the Need for Healthcare

THE USE OF THE 'ARBUTHNOTT INDEX' IN ESTIMATING HEALTHCARE NEEDS

3.15   It is important to emphasise that this index is not a *direct measure* of healthcare needs. It is a measure of the main factors that *influence* healthcare needs. The next step is to estimate for each care programme the extent to which the relative healthcare needs of populations in different areas of Scotland are influenced by this index. This estimate is obtained by statistical analysis of the relationship between the use of services and the new index at small area level, after taking into account differences in access to services and differences in Health Board policies. Figure 3.7 provides an example based on the statistical evidence of the relationship between the use of services for respiratory diseases and the 'Arbuthnott index'. A sample of postcode sectors for Greater Glasgow is used in Figure 3.7 to illustrate the method, but the analysis is based on data for Scotland as a whole.

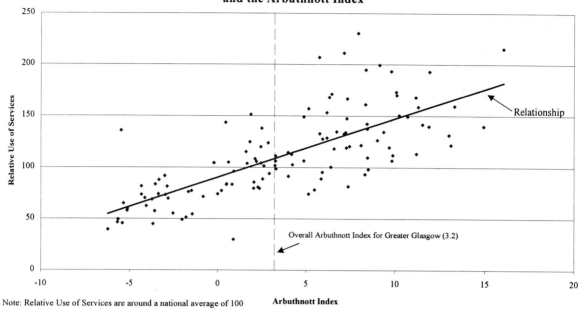

Figure 3.7: Relationship Between the Use of Services for Respiratory Diseases and the Arbuthnott Index

Note: Relative Use of Services are around a national average of 100
This illustration is based on Greater Glasgow Health Board postcode sectors

3.16   The strength of this relationship between the use of services and the 'Arbuthnott index' varies between care programmes. For example, Figure 3.8 shows as examples the estimated relationship for two of the acute hospital services: cancer services and respiratory diseases. The relationships indicate that this index has a much stronger influence on the use of respiratory services than on the use of cancer services. This is consistent with other evidence which shows that the incidence of respiratory disease is strongly linked with deprivation, whereas there is not such a close relationship overall between cancer and deprivation - though some cancers (e.g. lung cancer) are closely associated with deprivation.

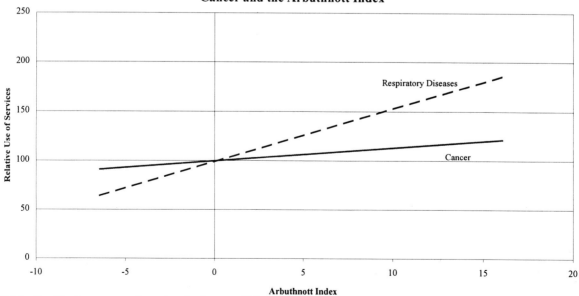

Figure 3.8: Relationship Between the Use of Services for Respiratory Diseases and Cancer and the Arbuthnott Index

Relative Use of Services are expressed around a national average of 100
This illustration is based on all postcode sectors

3.17   Table 3.1 shows the strength of the relationship between the 'Arbuthnott index' and the use of services for all of the care programmes and disease groups covered in this review. The strength varies considerably from one area to another because deprivation has a greater impact on the need for healthcare in some services than in others. For example, deprivation strongly influences the relative need for care in schizophrenia, substance misuse, and learning disabilities. It has a much weaker effect on the relative need for maternity services. **However, the results of this analysis show that to some degree deprivation has an influence on needs in every area of healthcare.**

Table 3.1: Strength of the Relationship Between the 'Arbuthnott index' and the Use of Services in 1997-98

Care Programme and Diagnostic Group	Strength of Relationship
Acute	
Cancer	1.887
circulatory diseases	4.310
respiratory diseases	6.833
diseases of the digestive system	4.762
injuries and poisonings	5.634
other acute	3.681
Mental Illness	
Schizophrenia	11.234
Dementia	4.509
non-psychotic conditions	6.513
substance misuse	15.637
other mental illness	4.643
Care of the Elderly	4.358
Maternity	0.420
Learning Disabilities	11.582
Community	
district nursing	4.590
heath visiting	2.434
GP Prescribing	
Gastrointestinal	4.754
Circulatory	3.284
mental illness	4.230
Infections	0.171
musculoskeletal and joint diseases	6.556
other GP prescribing	2.866

Note: the strength of the relationship represents the coefficient on the 'Arbuthnott index'

3.18   The Steering Group considers that the use of a single index in estimating the influence of morbidity and life circumstances on the need for healthcare has a number of advantages.

- This approach continues to be evidence based. The selection of four key indicators is based on evidence which shows that they are closely associated with the use of health services.

- Estimates of the strength of the relationship between the use of services and the 'Arbuthnott index' are also based on evidence. The analysis of this relationship is still done separately for each care programme and for disease groups within these programmes.

- The four indicators included in the index are generally recognised as closely linked with healthcare needs.

- The index is very stable. The estimates of the index for each Health Board in 1996-97 and 1997-98 in Figure 3.6 show little change between the 2 years.

- The index represents a useful combination of indicators which can be updated each year (the mortality rate among people under 65, the unemployment rate, and elderly people on income support) and an index based on data from the 1991 Census (households with two or more indicators of deprivation). This should ensure that the index is responsive to changing circumstances.

- Overall this approach has much greater transparency.

3.19   The approach that the Steering Group is proposing has obvious similarities to the Carstairs index of deprivation which has been widely used in analysing the relationship between deprivation and health in Scotland. The Carstairs index is also based on equal weighting of four indicators of deprivation: male unemployment; social class; overcrowded housing conditions; and car ownership. However, the selection of the four indicators in the 'Arbuthnott index' is not based on judgement; it is based on evidence that these four indicators are closely associated with the relative need for healthcare.

3.20   A criticism of the Carstairs index is that giving equal weight to the different indicators is arbitrary, and the same criticism might be levelled at the new index. The Steering Group has looked at the sensitivity of the index to alternative methods of weighting the four indicators together, and the results which are set out in Appendix E suggest that whatever weighting system is adopted the index is very similar.

3.21   The use of indicators from the 1991 census in *Fair Shares for All* was felt by some of those who commented during consultation to be a disadvantage since the data may be out of date. There are two points to note about this. First, the purpose of a resource allocation formula is to estimate the *relative* need for healthcare resources. While there may have been general changes during the 1990s in overall socio-economic circumstances (e.g. the general level of unemployment), the *relative* position of different areas of Scotland will not have changed substantially. Areas that were relatively deprived during the 1991 census remain relatively deprived. Second, current healthcare needs are influenced by the past circumstances in which people lived as well as by their current circumstances. Information about socio-economic circumstances from the 1991 census is relevant to current healthcare needs. This information will of course be updated at the next census in 2001.

RESULTS

3.22   An important requirement of this new approach to the adjustment for morbidity and life circumstances is that it should produce estimates of the relative need for healthcare that are quite stable from one year to the next. Figure 3.9 compares the estimated indices of relative healthcare needs for HCHS and GP prescribing for 1996-97 and 1997-98. The estimates for both years are very similar and therefore the model that has been developed shows a high degree of stability. The estimates for the island Health Boards also show a high degree of stability between the 2 years.

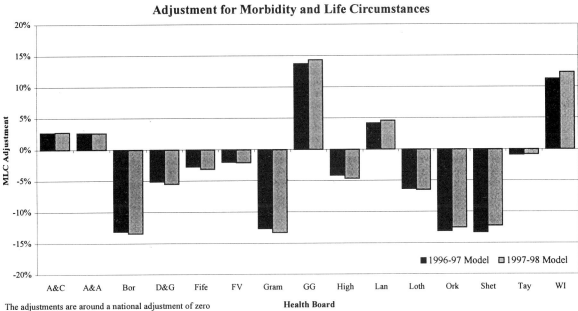

Figure 3.9: Relative Need for Resources Compared to National Average
(Arbuthnott Index Models)
Adjustment for Morbidity and Life Circumstances

The adjustments are around a national adjustment of zero

3.23   The pattern of relative needs between Health Boards in Figure 3.9 is obviously similar to the pattern of the 'Arbuthnott index' in Figure 3.6. This reflects the fact that Health Boards which have a relatively high value for the 'Arbuthnott index' are Boards with relatively high levels of deprivation and therefore relatively high needs for healthcare. However it is the scale of these relative healthcare needs that has to be estimated and this has been done by looking at the strength of the relationship between the index and the use of services.

3.24   Figure 3.10 shows how the revised estimate of relative needs (for 1997-98) compares with the estimate in *Fair Shares for All*. The pattern of relative need is broadly similar, though there are some significant differences for certain Boards.

Figure 3.10: Relative Need for Resources Compared to National Average
Adjustment for Morbidity and Life Circumstances

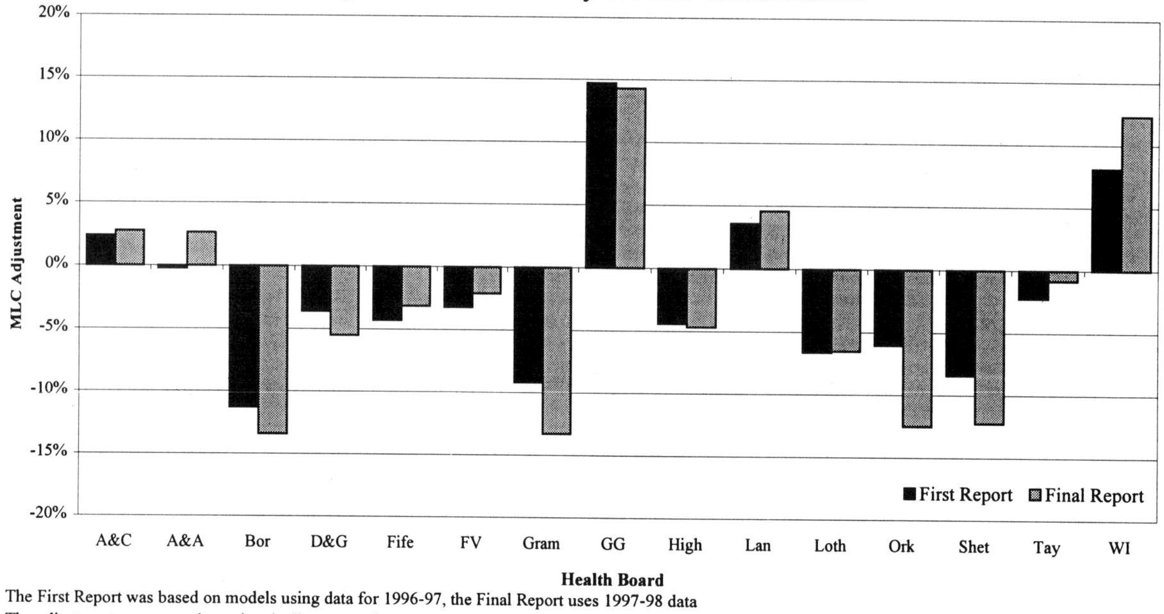

The First Report was based on models using data for 1996-97, the Final Report uses 1997-98 data
The adjustments are around a national adjustment of zero

3.25   The evidence that has been produced through this analysis of the relationship between the 'Arbuthnott index' and the use of health services is consistent with other studies which have also shown a strong association between deprivation and health. The Black Report[2] in 1980 looked at the evidence on inequalities in health related to social class and concluded that there were substantial differences and that these inequalities were largely related to socio-economic circumstances. The Acheson Report[3] in 1998 reviewed the evidence and found that although there had been general improvements in health over the past 50 years, there still remained significant inequalities. Within Scotland, the study by Carstairs and Morris[4] looked at the relationship between deprivation and a range of indicators of morbidity and mortality at small area level, and the results of their analysis showed that relatively affluent areas had lower levels of morbidity and mortality than more affluent areas. McLaren and Bain[5] recently used a similar approach to analyse the relationship between deprivation and health in the national priority services: cancer, coronary heart disease, and mental health. Again, their work showed that in each of these areas there is evidence of a strong association between health and deprivation.

CONCLUSIONS

3.26   The treatment of morbidity and life circumstances in a resource allocation formula has been thoroughly and carefully examined in this review of the responses received during consultation. We have sought to achieve greater transparency in the analysis of the influence

2 Department of Health and Social Security. Inequalities in Health: Report of a Working Party Chaired by Sir Douglas Black. DHSS London 1980.

3 D Acheson. Independent Inquiry into Inequalities in Health: Report. London 1998

4 V Carstairs and R Morris. Deprivation and Health in Scotland. Aberdeen University Press 1991

5 G McLaren and M Bain. Deprivation and Health in Scotland: Insights from NHS Data. Information and Statistics Division, Common Services Agency. Edinburgh 1998

of this important factor in relative healthcare needs, while at the same time retaining the essential evidence based approach that was adopted in *Fair Shares for All*. The Steering Group consider that the use of a single index, the 'Arbuthnott index', meets these aims. The selection of the indicators included in the index is based on evidence and the estimates of the influence of this index on the use of services across the different care programmes is also based on evidence. Through the use of several indicators that can be updated annually the index should be responsive to changes over time in the relative healthcare needs of different population groups, yet the allocations to which it gives rise should be stable enough from year to year to allow Health Boards to plan service delivery strategically.

CHAPTER 4:
REMOTENESS

4.1   *Fair Shares for All* recommended that an adjustment should be introduced into the resource allocation formula to take account of the additional costs of delivering hospital and community health services to populations living in remote and rural areas of Scotland. The only adjustment for the effects of remoteness in the present SHARE formula is limited to an allowance for the extra costs of district nursing and health visiting.

4.2   Estimates of the influence of remoteness on the costs of delivering hospital services were based on an analysis of the relationship between the costs to Health Boards of securing hospital care for their residents and a number of indicators of remoteness. The *relative* level of hospital costs in each Health Board was calculated by comparing actual expenditure on services in each Board with the level of expenditure that would be expected if these services were purchased at Scottish average costs. This ratio of actual to expected costs tends to be significantly higher among Health Boards with a high proportion of their population living in remote and rural areas. The main reason for this is that small hospitals have to be provided in remote and rural areas to make services accessible to patients, and these hospitals incur relatively high costs per patient largely because they do not enjoy the economies of scale of large hospitals in urban areas. For example, in a large hospital it may be possible to manage a sickness absence in medical staff within existing resources, but in a small hospital it will usually be necessary to employ a locum at considerable additional cost to provide cover. In smaller hospitals the unit costs of services such as catering and laundry tend to be higher because of the more limited scope for spreading fixed costs. Small hospitals may not be able to use expensive equipment as intensively as in a large hospital, and in rural areas they may also face higher costs for supplies because of additional transport costs.

4.3   The main indicators of remoteness in each Health Board that were used in the analysis in *Fair Shares for All* were population density and the proportion of the Health Board's population living in communities of less than 500, 1,000 or 10,000 people.

4.4   The main issues raised during consultation included:

- the possible influence of other indicators on hospital costs;
- the implications of estimating separate adjustments for the effect of remoteness on hospital costs for each of the three island Boards rather than applying a uniform adjustment to them;
- the need to ensure a consistent treatment of the remoteness issue between the three island Boards and island communities in other Health Board areas;
- the treatment in the proposed adjustment of Health Boards such as Argyll and Clyde which have a mix of urban and rural areas.

OTHER INDICATORS

4.5   The further work that has been done has considered a number of other indicators. These included alternative methods of measuring population density such as the arithmetic mean and the geometric mean, other indicators of remoteness (e.g. the average number of road kilometres per 1,000 population), and other possible influences on relative Health Board costs.

4.6   The only indicator which seems to provide a better measure of the influence of remoteness on hospital costs than the indicators previously used in *Fair Shares for All* is the number of road kilometres per 1,000 population. Figure 4.1 shows for each Health Board the average number of road kilometres per 1,000 population over the 3 year period 1996-98. The Health Boards fall into a number of broad groups:

- the island Health Boards where the average number of road kilometres per 1,000 population is 62;
- three mainland Health Boards (Borders, Dumfries and Galloway, and Highland) where road kilometres per 1,000 population are about 30-40;
- three mainland Boards (Argyll and Clyde, Grampian, and Tayside) where the value of this indicator lies within the range 10-20; and
- the six remaining mainland Boards where the number of road kilometres is less than 10 per 1,000 population.

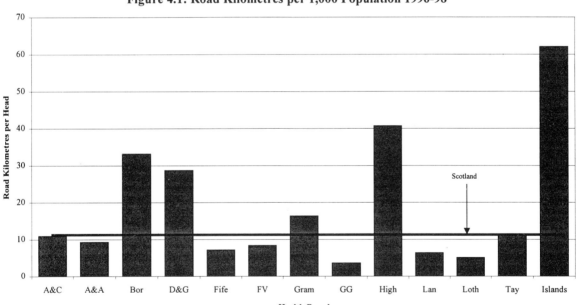

Figure 4.1: Road Kilometres per 1,000 Population 1996-98

Note: the roads included in this measure cover principal, A, B, C, unclassified roads and all trunk roads
The principal, A, B, C and unclassified roads include built up, non-built up, dual and single

4.7   Road kilometres per 1,000 population may provide a better indicator of the effects of remoteness on the costs of hospital services because it reflects more closely the extent to which communities are dispersed, and this is the factor that influences the need to make services more accessible by providing small hospitals in remote and rural areas. It may be worth emphasising that road kilometres per 1,000 population is not a **direct measure** of the factors that influence the costs of hospital services. It is an **indicator** of remoteness and the influence that this in turn has on the costs of providing hospital care. Estimates have been made of the relationship between this indicator and the relative costs of providing hospital services for the residents of each Health Board area. In Health Boards with a relatively high number of road kilometres per 1,000 population the average cost of providing hospital services for their residents is significantly above the national average.

4.8   Figure 4.2 shows the relative adjustment for the costs of hospital services in each Health Board based on the relationship between costs and road kilometres per 1,000 population. This revised adjustment is compared with the earlier adjustment published in *Fair Shares for All*.

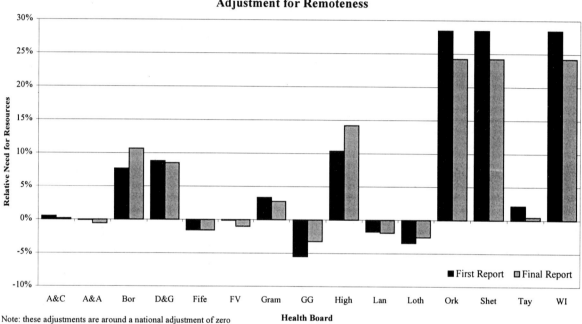

Figure 4.2: Relative Need for Resources Compared to National Average: Adjustment for Remoteness

Note: these adjustments are around a national adjustment of zero

The pattern of adjustment is broadly similar to that published in *Fair Shares for All* though there are some differences to note:

- the three island Health Boards still receive a substantial adjustment though it is somewhat smaller than the adjustment proposed in *Fair Shares for All* (24.2% compared with 28.5%);

- some of the mainland Boards (Borders and Highland) with substantial rural areas will gain from the revised adjustment;

- for some of the more urban Boards (Greater Glasgow and Lothian) that would experience a reduction in their allocation as a result of this adjustment, the reduction is smaller than proposed in *Fair Shares for All*.

4.9   The Steering Group has considered carefully a number of issues about this adjustment for the additional costs of hospital services.

- First, whether a further adjustment is required to take account of the particular position of the three island Health Boards (and island communities in other Health Board areas).

- Second, whether the same adjustment should be made to the three island Health Boards or whether a separate adjustment should be estimated for each island Board.

- Third, whether this method of adjusting the allocation formula for remoteness adequately reflects the position of Health Boards such as Argyll and Clyde which, though predominantly urban, have a significant proportion of their population living in remote and rural areas.

- Finally, some concerns were expressed during consultation about the scale of the adjustment proposed for the effects of remoteness on hospital costs and the quality of the evidence to support this proposal.

ISLAND HEALTH BOARDS

4.10   The proposed formula would provide a substantial adjustment of almost 25% to allow for the additional costs of providing hospital care in island Health Boards and the Steering Group has considered carefully whether any further adjustment is required to take account of the particular problems of delivering hospital care in island Health Boards.

4.11   The factor that distinguishes the island Health Boards (and island communities generally) from 'rural' mainland Boards is the greater difficulties faced in travelling to large mainland hospitals for treatment. Where patients from these island communities are sent to large mainland hospitals for treatment then the costs of treatment will generally be the same as the costs of treating patients from urban areas. (Clearly there are significant costs associated with patient travel to the mainland, but these costs are funded separately and are not covered in this review.) However, a high proportion of the population in the island Boards is treated locally in relatively small hospitals and this means that the overall impact of remoteness on their costs is much greater than is the case in a rural mainland Board.

4.12   The proposed adjustment for remoteness is based on evidence about the extent to which the costs of providing access to hospital services is higher in remote and rural areas. This evidence clearly shows that the three island Health Boards face costs which are substantially higher than any mainland Health Board and this is reflected in the adjustment of 25%. We have not found any evidence to suggest that an even higher adjustment is needed to reflect the additional costs of providing hospital services in island areas.

A UNIFORM ADJUSTMENT FOR THE THREE ISLAND HEALTH BOARDS

4.13   In *Fair Shares for All* a uniform adjustment was proposed for the additional costs of providing hospital care in the three island Health Boards. During consultation it was suggested that it might be more appropriate to estimate separate adjustments for these Boards. Separate adjustments are proposed in estimating the effects of remoteness on the costs of providing community health services and general medical services, and a separate adjustment is also proposed for the effects of morbidity and life circumstances.

4.14   Having considered this issue the Steering Group does not feel that separate adjustments should be applied to each of the island Health Boards to take account of the additional costs of providing **hospital** care. There are some differences between the three island Health Boards in the distribution of their population - for example the percentage of the population living in communities of less than 500 people is larger in Orkney than in

Shetland and the Western Isles. However, there is no evidence to suggest that these differences are material enough to give rise to differences in the relative costs of providing hospital care in one island Board compared with another. The Steering Group considers that all three island Health Boards (and island communities in other Health Board areas) face essentially the same scale of additional costs in providing hospital care. A uniform adjustment of almost 25% to allow for this provides the fairest method of taking into account the effects of island status on hospital costs within a resource allocation formula.

IMPLICATIONS FOR MAINLAND HEALTH BOARDS

4.15   Some mainland Health Boards cannot easily be classified as 'urban' or 'rural'. Most are, in fact, a mixture of urban and rural areas. Argyll and Clyde provides a good example. Most of the population in Argyll and Clyde lives in densely populated urban areas, but a significant proportion lives in remote and rural areas on the mainland north of the Clyde, and a small proportion (about 3.5%) lives on islands. During consultation some concerns were raised about whether the method of adjusting the formula for remoteness took account of this variation *within* Health Board areas.

4.16   The proposed adjustment for the effect of remoteness of hospital services takes into account the average number of road kilometres per 1,000 population in each Health Board. Table 4.1 shows how this figure differs between Council areas within Argyll and Clyde Health Board.

Table 4.1: Road Kilometres per 1,000 Population by Council Area within Argyll and Clyde in 1996

Council Area	Population	Road Km per 1,000 Population
Argyll & Bute	90,840	32.28 km
West Dumbartonshire	49,180	3.38 km
East Renfrewshire	24,830	5.28 km
Inverclyde	87,100	4.81 km
Refrewshire	178,550	5.09 km
Total	430,500	10.67 km

4.17   Rural areas within Argyll and Clyde (e.g. Argyll and Bute) have significantly higher road kilometres per 1,000 population than the more densely populated urban areas (e.g. West Dumbartonshire). However the **average** figure for Argyll and Clyde Health Board as a whole reflects the variation in road kilometres per 1,000 population in different areas within the Board. The greater remoteness of areas such as Argyll and Bute is taken into account because it is reflected in this average figure for the board as a whole. This average is significantly higher than the average for other 'urban' Boards such as Greater Glasgow and Lanarkshire.

4.18   It is useful to compare the remoteness adjustment for Argyll and Clyde with the adjustment for other Health Boards with densely populated urban areas such as Lanarkshire, Lothian, and Greater Glasgow (Figure 4.2). Argyll and Clyde's adjustment is slightly above the national average while the adjustments for Lanarkshire, Lothian and Greater Glasgow are significantly below the national average. This difference reflects the extent to which Argyll and Clyde's adjustment is influenced by the significant proportion of its population who live in remote and rural areas.

4.19   The proposed adjustment for the effects of remoteness on the costs of providing community health services was set out in *Fair Shares for All* and the Steering Group do not consider that any revision is required to this part of the formula. The implications of remoteness for the costs of providing general medical services are discussed in Chapter 6.

QUALITY OF EVIDENCE

4.20   The Steering Group has reviewed the evidence about the influence of remoteness on costs and is satisfied that:

(a) there is a need for an adjustment to take account of the additional costs of providing hospital and community health services in remote and rural areas. The absence of such an adjustment is a serious weakness in the current SHARE formula;

(b) the evidence shows that the adjustment required to take account of the effect of remoteness on the costs of providing hospital and community health services should be significant;

(c) the island Health Boards (and island communities in other Boards) face particular difficulties and require a substantial adjustment;

4.21   This review represents the first attempt to assess systematically the effects of remote and rural areas on Health Boards' need for resources. Further work needs to be done over the next few years to improve and refine these estimates, but the Steering Group considers that the estimates provide a sound basis on which to begin to incorporate an adjustment for remote and rural areas into a resource allocation formula.

CHAPTER 5:
RESULTS FOR HOSPITAL AND COMMUNITY HEALTH SERVICES AND GP PRESCRIBING

5.1   This chapter outlines the revised estimates of relative need for resources for HCHS and GP prescribing, and sets out the implications for expenditure in each Health Board over the period 2000-01 to 2003-04.

RELATIVE NEEDS

5.2   Table 5.1 shows the revised estimates of relative need as a result of three factors: the age and sex structure of the population; morbidity and life circumstances; and the effects of remoteness. The final column of this table shows the combined effects of these factors on the relative need of each Health Board for resources for the care programmes covered by hospital and community health services and GP prescribing.

5.3   The estimates of relative need in each Board are shown as the percentage difference in the resources required per head of population from the national average. Taking Borders Health Board as an example:

- Borders requires 10.4% more resources per head of population than the national average because it has a high proportion of people over the age of 65 and this adds significantly to the demands placed on healthcare.
- Borders' relative need for resources as a result of morbidity and life circumstances is 13.4% below the national average, reflecting the low levels of morbidity and deprivation in this area of Scotland.
- Its need for resources as a result of remoteness is 9.0% above the national average.
- The combined influence of these factors - in the final Column - indicates that Borders' relative need for resources for HCHS and GP prescribing is 4.0% above the national average.

5.4   The final column of Table 5.1 shows the extent to which the estimates of relative need for healthcare resources differ between Health Board areas in Scotland. The most striking feature is the difference in the estimate of relative need in Western Isles. At 48% above the national average this is much higher than for any other Board. The important point to note, however, is that Western Isles is unique within Scotland in that it has relatively high needs in relation to **all** of the factors that influence these needs. It has a relatively high proportion of elderly people; it has high levels of deprivation; and it also faces significant additional costs in delivering services in remote and rural areas. No other Health Board in Scotland faces this unique set of circumstances, and this accounts for the exceptionally high overall estimate of Western Isles' relative need for resources.

Table 5.1: Relative Need for Resources (Percentage Difference from National Average) Hospital and Community Health Services and GP Prescribing

Health Board	Age/Sex Adjustment %	Morbidity and Life Circumstances Adjustment %	Remoteness Adjustment %	Overall Adjustment %
Argyll & Clyde	0.1	2.8	0.3	3.2
Ayrshire & Arran	2.3	2.6	-0.7	4.4
Borders	10.4	-13.4	9.0	4.0
Dumfries & Galloway	7.9	-5.5	7.1	9.2
Fife	1.2	-3.1	-1.4	-3.3
Forth Valley	-0.7	-2.1	-1.0	-3.7
Grampian	-2.2	-13.3	2.1	-13.5
Greater Glasgow	-0.9	14.3	-3.2	9.6
Highland	1.8	-4.7	13.2	9.8
Lanarkshire	-5.5	4.6	-1.9	-3.1
Lothian	-1.7	-6.5	-2.5	-10.4
Orkney	3.1	-12.5	18.9	7.2
Shetland	-4.1	-12.2	20.4	1.3
Tayside	5.5	-0.8	0.1	4.8
Western Isles	9.4	12.3	20.4	48.2

Note: the overall adjustment is calculated at the care programme level by a) converting these percentages into index numbers around 1 (0%=1, +50%=1.5, -50%=0.5) then b) multiplying together the adjustments for age/sex, MLC and remoteness. For example Dumfries & Galloway = 1.079*0.945*1.071=1.092 or 9.2%
Any discrepancies between the total and the individual factors are due to rounding.

5.5   It is more usual to find that a Board has relative high needs because of some factors and relatively low needs because of other factors. It is important to bear in mind that Boards which appear similar in some respects may be quite different in other respects. Some examples may illustrate this.

5.6   During consultation it was suggested that the different estimates of relative needs in the island Health Boards is surprising. These three Boards certainly face similar difficulties in delivering services to remote communities, but they differ significantly in other respects. Western Isles has a high proportion of elderly people over the age of 65 and its population has relatively high levels of deprivation compared with Orkney and Shetland.

5.7   Argyll and Clyde and Lanarkshire have significant levels of deprivation but the estimates of their overall relative needs are somewhat different. Lanarkshire has a relatively young population while Argyll and Clyde's age structure is very close to the national average. Levels of morbidity and deprivation are in fact somewhat higher in Lanarkshire than in Argyll and Clyde. There are also differences in the effects of remoteness. Because a significant proportion of Argyll and Clyde's population lives in remote and rural areas the adjustment for remoteness is above the adjustment in Lanarkshire.

CHANGES FROM CURRENT ALLOCATION SHARES

5.8   Table 5.2 shows the changes in each Health Board's share of HCHS and GP prescribing resources as a result of the proposed formula compared with current shares.

Table 5.2: Current and Target Shares of HCHS and GP Prescribing Resources

Health Board	Current Allocation Share %	New Allocation Share %	Change in Share %
Scotland	100.0	100.0	0.0
Argyll & Clyde	8.62	8.47	-1.7
Ayrshire & Arran	7.33	7.54	3.0
Borders	2.13	2.11	-1.0
Dumfries & Galloway	3.08	3.10	0.9
Fife	6.38	6.45	1.1
Forth Valley	5.13	5.12	-0.1
Grampian	9.50	9.08	-4.4
Greater Glasgow	19.10	19.61	2.7
Highland	4.12	4.42	7.2
Lanarkshire	10.34	10.43	0.9
Lothian	14.16	13.69	-3.3
Orkney	0.43	0.42	-2.3
Shetland	0.53	0.47	-10.1
Tayside	8.38	8.24	-1.7
Western Isles	0.79	0.84	6.0

Note: the current share is based on the allocations to Health Boards for HCHS and GP prescribing in 2000-01. This share takes into account the special islands allowance allocated to the three island Health Boards.

IMPLICATIONS FOR HEALTH BOARD ALLOCATIONS

5.9   The implications for each Health Board's expenditure of these changes in the share of resources will depend on a number of factors including: the overall growth in resources over the next few years, the pace of change towards the new targets, and population changes. It would be quite wrong to infer from these figures that a Health Board whose *share* of resources is reduced will also experience a reduction in its *actual* resources. The Minister for Health and Community Care has given a commitment that all Health Boards will receive real terms growth in their resources during the lifetime of the Scottish Parliament.

5.10   To assess trends in the allocation of funding for HCHS and GP prescribing to each Health Board the following assumptions have been made.

- Total expenditure on HCHS and GP prescribing will increase by 5.5% annually between the period 2000-01 and 2003-04.

- In 2001-02 all Health Boards will receive **at least** the indicative increases in funding of which they have already been notified. In subsequent years each Board is assumed to receive an increase in funding of at least 4.0% annually.

- The growth money over and above the minimum amounts allocated to Boards will be targeted on those Boards whose allocation share needs to rise.

- The projections of the allocation shares for Health Boards have been adjusted to take account of projected changes in population shares.

- The estimates of future allocations to each Board have been adjusted to 2000-01 prices using the GDP deflator. This index of inflation is assumed to increase by 2.5% a year between 2000-01 and 2003-04.

46

5.11   **It must be emphasised that the projections of Health Board expenditure based on these assumptions should be seen as illustrative.** It is not possible to forecast all of the factors that will influence trends in allocation shares, and some of the assumptions made are subject to uncertainty. In particular it is worth noting that:

- Trends in allocation shares will be influenced by changes in the age and sex structure of the population in different Health Boards as well as by changes in the 'Arbuthnott index' which measures the influence of morbidity and life circumstances on relative healthcare needs. It is not possible to forecast at this stage precisely how these factors are likely to change over the next few years.

- The projections of population used in this illustration are subject to some uncertainty, and indeed it was for this reason that we recommend that Mid-Year Population Estimates should be used in the allocation formula. However in assessing future trends in allocations some account must be taken of population changes and the population projections produced by the General Register Office for Scotland are the only figures that can be used for this purpose.

- Estimates of future trends in the overall level of expenditure and inflation are also subject to some uncertainty.

5.12   Table 5.3 shows the indicative trends in the funds allocated to each Board for HCHS and GP prescribing over the period 2000-01 to 2003-04 based on the assumptions outlined in paragraph 5.10. These expenditure figures are at 2000-01 prices. On these assumptions, total expenditure would increase in 2000-01 prices from £4,141.8m in 2000-01 to £4,516.5m in 2003-04, a rise of £374.7m (9.0%). Furthermore, all Health Boards would experience growth in real terms in the resources allocated for HCHS and GP prescribing over this period.

Table 5.3: Illustrative Health Board Allocations for HCHS and GP Prescribing at 2000-01 Prices

Health Board	2000-01 £m	2001-02 £m	2002-03 £m	2003-04 £m	Change 2000-01 to 2003-04 £m
Scotland	4,141.8	4,263.3	4,388.1	4,516.5	374.7
Argyll & Clyde	356.9	366.0	371.4	380.0	23.1
Ayrshire & Arran	303.5	314.2	327.8	339.1	35.6
Borders	88.3	90.6	92.9	96.0	7.7
Dumfries & Galloway	127.5	130.7	135.4	139.8	12.4
Fife	264.2	273.0	282.8	292.5	28.2
Forth Valley	212.4	217.2	224.1	231.9	19.5
Grampian	393.4	401.1	406.9	412.9	19.5
Greater Glasgow	790.9	820.5	851.9	879.1	88.3
Highland	170.8	179.0	191.8	200.1	29.3
Lanarkshire	428.1	441.7	456.3	471.5	43.4
Lothian	586.4	601.6	610.4	625.7	39.2
Orkney	17.8	18.4	18.6	19.0	1.1
Shetland	21.8	22.1	22.5	22.8	1.0
Tayside	347.0	353.3	359.4	369.2	22.2
Western Isles	32.7	34.0	35.8	37.0	4.2

Note: the money covers the unified budget allocations to Health Boards for Hospital and Community Health Services and GP prescribing in 2000-01. This share takes into account the special islands allowance allocated to the three island Health Boards, and excludes GMS cash limited and 'out of hours' services.

5.13   Table 5.4 shows the trends in expenditure per head after taking into account the projected changes in population between 2000-01 and 2003-04. Again, all Health Boards will experience significant growth in expenditure per head (at 2000-01 prices) between 2000-01 and 2003-04.

Table 5.4: Illustrative Expenditure per Head on HCHS and GP Prescribing at 2000-01 Prices

Health Board	2000-01 £ per Head	2001-02 £ per Head	2002-03 £ per Head	2003-04 £ per Head	Change 2000-01 to 2003-04 £ per Head
Scotland	809	834	859	884	75
Argyll & Clyde	836	861	876	899	63
Ayrshire & Arran	809	839	877	908	99
Borders	830	852	873	901	71
Dumfries & Galloway	865	888	921	953	87
Fife	757	782	809	837	80
Forth Valley	770	787	811	837	67
Grampian	749	766	777	789	40
Greater Glasgow	868	903	940	973	105
Highland	820	859	920	959	139
Lanarkshire	763	788	814	841	78
Lothian	758	775	784	801	43
Orkney	913	938	953	972	60
Shetland	953	968	983	997	44
Tayside	890	910	928	956	65
Western Isles	1,172	1,227	1,304	1,355	183

Note: the money covers the unified budget allocations to Health Boards for Hospital and Community Health Services and GP prescribing in 2000-01. This share takes into account the special islands allowance allocated to the three island Health Boards, and excludes GMS cash limited and 'out of hours' services.

PROGRESS TOWARDS NEW TARGET SHARES

5.14   Under the assumptions used in these forward projections of expenditure, progress towards the target allocation shares (including the effects of population changes) would be quite rapid. By 2003-04 all Health Boards other than Shetland and Grampian will be very close to their target allocation. These illustrations assume that national growth in the resources available for HCHS and GP prescribing continues at 5.5% per annum throughout this period. It is for Ministers to decide upon the rate at which progress should be made towards the new allocation shares.

CONCLUSIONS

5.15   The projections of expenditure (and expenditure per head) at Health Board level need to be treated with some caution. They are based on a range of assumptions about key factors and there are other factors, such as changes in the 'Arbuthnott index', which have not been taken into account. Subject to these caveats, the projections indicate that:

- substantial progress can be made towards the new target allocation shares over the next 3 years; and
- during this period all Health Boards will continue to see growth in real terms in the resources available for HCHS and GP prescribing.

CHAPTER 6:
GENERAL MEDICAL SERVICES

6.1   *Fair Shares for All* recommended that for the first time a formula should be introduced to determine the most equitable method of allocating resources for General Medical Services (GMS) between Health Boards. The GMS care programme covers two elements with distinct methods of resource distribution:

- A non cash limited allocation covering fees and payments made to GPs
- A cash limited allocation to cover the costs of staffing (excluding Independent Contractor GPs), IT/computing costs and most premises costs.

6.2   Because of its innovative nature this particular recommendation attracted a good deal of comment during consultation. To ensure that these comments were considered comprehensively, the Steering Group set up a separate Working Group to review the GMS work and to provide the Steering Group with advice. This Working Group included representatives of the Scottish General Practitioners Committee, academics with a special interest in GMS, a Chief Executive of a Primary Care Trust, and information and statistical advisers. Full details of the membership of this sub-group is set out in Annex B.

6.3   The main areas of concern raised during consultation included:

- the relevance of a resource allocation formula based on need to GMS;
- the representativeness of the data from the Continuous Morbidity Recording scheme used in the analysis;
- the coverage of work carried out in GMS in the Continuous Morbidity Recording scheme;
- the use of postcode sector data;
- the adjustment for remoteness and the treatment of inducement practices.

RELEVANCE OF A RESOURCE ALLOCATION FORMULA TO GMS

6.4   Some of the comments received during consultation on *Fair Shares for All* suggested that it is inappropriate to apply an allocation formula based on estimates of relative need to GMS because these services are essentially demand led. The Steering Group has considered this issue carefully and remain convinced that basic objective of this review, i.e. to ensure that resources are allocated between Health Boards to achieve equity of access to healthcare, is as relevant to GMS as it is to Hospital and Community Health Services and to GP prescribing. Relative needs for GMS are influenced by the same factors that influence relative needs for other services: the age and sex structure of the population, morbidity and life circumstances, and remoteness. There may well be practical issues that will need to be considered about the implementation of a resource allocation formula in GMS because of the particular non cash limited aspects of this service. However, this does not detract from the importance of ensuring that the relative needs of different population groups are taken into account in allocating these resources.

REPRESENTATIVENESS

6.5   The data used in the analysis of relative needs for GMS services in *Fair Shares for All* was taken from the Continuous Morbidity Recording (CMR) scheme which collects information about face-to-face consultations between GPs and patients from a sample of GMS practices. This data was used to estimate the influence of the age and sex structure of the population and morbidity and life circumstances on the relative need for GMS services. The representativeness of the CMR data was examined by the Working Group.

6.6   The practices that participate in the CMR scheme differ in some respects from practices nationally. In particular they are more likely to draw their populations from rural areas and less likely to draw their patients from deprived areas, particularly areas of concentrated deprivation. The CMR practices are more likely to be training practices, tend to be larger partnerships and have higher levels of activities which are linked to item-of-service fees. The age and sex characteristics of the populations registered with CMR practices are broadly representative of Scotland as a whole.

6.7   The key issue, however, is whether the CMR practices provide information about the relative use of services by different population groups that is representative nationally of the use made of GMS. It is this information about the **relative** use of services that is important in determining the allocation of resources. The evidence indicates that the difference in contact rates between affluent and deprived population groups in the CMR is not significantly different to that found in the Scottish Health Survey. The difference in prescribing costs between affluent and deprived CMR practices is comparable to the difference found between all affluent and all deprived Scottish practices. There is therefore no evidence that the estimates of relative need for affluent and deprived populations obtained from the CMR data are unrepresentative of the affluent and deprived groups in the population as a whole.

COVERAGE OF GMS

6.8   Some concerns were expressed during consultation that the CMR scheme only covers face to face consultations with GPs and does not take into account other aspects of the work of GMS, including telephone consultation, consultations with other members of the primary care team, the duration of consultations, and home visits. In response to these concerns the analysis has been extended to include night visits and also takes into account the influence of temporary residents on workload in GMS. Consideration was also given to including an adjustment to the CMR data to take account of differences in the duration of consultations with GPs, but because of the limited data available it was decided not to do so at present.

6.9   In carrying out further work in response to the comments made during consultation a number of improvements have been made to the formula proposed for GMS. These changes are described in the following sections.

REVISED FORMULA FOR GMS

POPULATION BASE

6.10   As explained in Chapter 2, the Steering Group considers that the Mid-Year Estimates of Population produced by the General Register Office for Scotland (GROS) provide the most appropriate basis for estimating Health Board population shares in a resource allocation formula. However, in reviewing the formula proposed for GMS the Steering Group has decided that the population estimates for this particular care programme should be based on the Community Health Index (CHI) of patients registered with GP practices.

6.11   The reason for adopting a different population estimate in GMS is that expenditure on these services by Health Boards is driven largely by the population registered with GPs and not by the actual population as reflected in Mid-Year Estimates. (As noted earlier, CHI registered populations tend to be higher than actual populations.) It would be inconsistent to fund Health Boards for GMS on the basis of one estimate of population while the payment system to GPs which Health Boards must use is based on a different population figure. In practice this anomaly between the CHI population figures and the Mid-Year Estimates produced by GROS should reduce as the quality of the CHI data improve.

ADJUSTMENT FOR POPULATION AGE AND SEX

6.12   Estimates of the relative needs of different age and sex groups for GMS are based primarily on CMR data on face-to-face contacts between patients and GPs for two years: 1996-97 and 1997-98. An adjustment has been included for contacts that involve home visits. Home visits have a larger implication for workload than surgery visits and the proportion of consultations accounted for by home visits increases with the age of the patient.

ADJUSTMENT FOR MORBIDITY AND LIFE CIRCUMSTANCES

6.13   The methods used to estimate the influence of morbidity and life circumstances on the relative need for resources in GMS are essentially the same as those used in other care programmes, though the analysis is now carried out at enumeration district level rather than postcode sector level. The reason for using the smaller enumeration districts in the GMS care programme is that the patients who are registered with a practice may be drawn from a wide area, and an assumption is required that the socio-economic characteristics of each area are relevant to the patients who come from that area. The smaller the area the less likely it is that this assumption will be invalid.

6.14   The 'Arbuthnott index' based on four indicators of morbidity and life circumstances has been used to estimate the influence of morbidity and life circumstances on the relative need for GMS resources. Figure 6.1 compares the Arbuthnott adjustment with an adjustment based on the Jarman index - a census-based index currently used to fund certain aspects of GMS payments. Although there is some similarity in the Boards which are above and below the national average using the two indices, the 'Arbuthnott index' appears to be a more sensitive indicator of relative need.

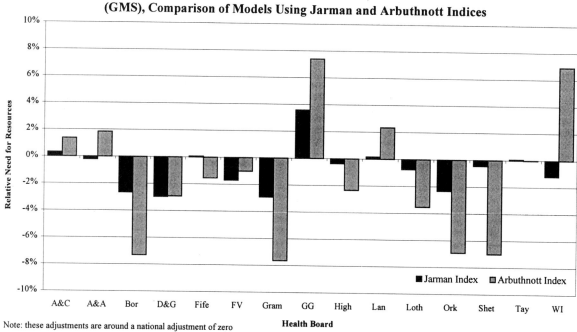

Figure 6.1: Relative Needs Adjustment for Morbidity and Life Circumstances (GMS), Comparison of Models Using Jarman and Arbuthnott Indices

Note: these adjustments are around a national adjustment of zero

Health Board

6.15   The revised adjustment for Morbidity and Life Circumstances takes into account the relative need for night visits as well as contacts with GPs. The relative Health Board needs in Figure 6.1 based on the 'Arbuthnott index' are broadly similar to the pattern seen in other care programmes, with Greater Glasgow, Western Isles, Lanarkshire, Argyll and Clyde, and Ayrshire and Arran having needs which are significantly above the average.

REMOTENESS

6.16   The method of estimating the effect of remoteness on the costs of providing GMS services has been revised. Total payments per patient (excluding those items outwith the scope of the Review) have been calculated from the GP payments database. Statistical analysis was then used to identify the influence of remoteness factors on the costs of delivering GMS. The information used to determine Rural Practice Payments was included as indicators of the amount of travel between GP surgeries and patient home addresses ("road mileage patients"). These indicators include an adjustment for travel by footpath and over water. The indicators that were found to be significant in this analysis were population density (hectares per person), the proportion of the population living in communities of less than 500 people, and the proportion of the practice list which qualify as road mileage patients.

6.17   Some concerns were raised during the consultation period that the method of analysis used in the Arbuthnott Review does not recognise the position of inducement practices in remote and rural areas. General Practitioners who work in sparsely populated areas may have significantly smaller lists than the Scottish average. As a substantial proportion of remuneration is related to the number of patients on the list (through the system of capitation fees), GPs in such areas will not receive a level of income expected in more populated areas. Under the Inducement Practitioner scheme, GPs can apply for an "income-guarantee" to ensure that they reach 82.4% of the level of intended income agreed by the Doctors' and

52

Dentists' Review Body. Because Inducement Practitioner GPs earn more income per patient than they would expect to earn in more populated areas, this manifests as a higher unit-cost of primary care in rural areas. Local factors will inform the exact location and qualification criteria for the Inducement Practitioner scheme. Nevertheless, they are a pertinent example of the additional costs of providing GMS in remote and rural areas and should be included in a general analysis of differences in primary care costs between rural and other areas. The inducement scheme is subject to partial review and this will need to be taken into account in applying this part of the formula.

6.18   The results of this revised analysis (and of the earlier published estimates) of the effects of remoteness are shown in Figure 6.2. There are several points to note:

- The estimates of the additional resources required in the island Health Boards are significantly lower than in the earlier published figures. These revised estimates are closer to the estimates of the effects of remoteness on the additional costs of providing hospital services and community health services in the islands.
- The estimates of the effects of remoteness on Borders and Dumfries and Galloway are now very similar.

Figure 6.2: Relative Need for Resources Compared to National Average (GMS): Adjustment for Remoteness

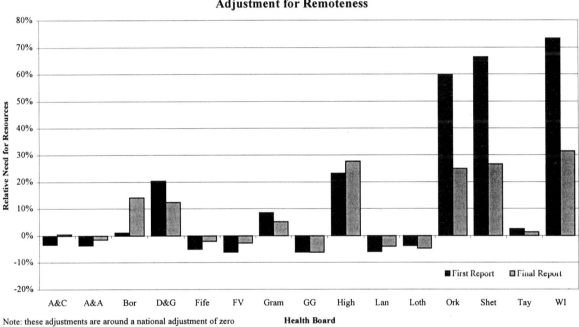

Note: these adjustments are around a national adjustment of zero   **Health Board**

TEMPORARY RESIDENTS

6.19   The number of claims for temporary residents varies considerably across Health Boards. In 1997-98, there were 180,000 claims for temporary residents (equivalent to 3.3% of the Scottish population). This percentage varies significantly between Health Board areas. In Highland the percentage was 11.3% while in Lanarkshire it was 2.8%. Because of the substantial differences in rates of temporary residents between Health Boards, an adjustment for this factor has been incorporated into the revised formula based on a weighting of 1.5 contacts per temporary resident.

OVERALL RESULTS

6.20   Table 6.1 shows the Health Board adjustments.

Table 6.1: Relative Need for Resources (Percentage Difference from National Average) General Medical Services

Health Board	Age/Sex Adjustment %	Morbidity and Life Circumstances Adjustment %	Remoteness Adjustment %	Overall Adjustment %
Scotland	0.0	0.0	0.0	0.0
Argyll & Clyde	0.0	1.8	0.5	2.5
Ayrshire & Arran	0.8	2.2	-1.5	1.6
Borders	3.3	-9.6	14.2	7.4
Dumfries & Galloway	2.4	-3.8	12.4	11.7
Fife	0.2	-2.2	-2.0	-4.0
Forth Valley	0.0	-1.4	-2.7	-4.1
Grampian	-1.2	-9.9	5.2	-6.2
Greater Glasgow	0.0	9.8	-6.2	2.3
Highland	0.1	-3.2	27.7	27.5
Lanarkshire	-1.6	3.0	-3.9	-3.4
Lothian	-0.3	-4.6	-4.6	-9.5
Orkney	0.3	-9.0	24.9	15.8
Shetland	-2.7	-9.0	26.6	13.4
Tayside	1.7	-0.1	1.4	3.2
Western Isles	1.3	8.8	31.4	47.9

Note: the overall adjustment includes temporary residents

6.21   Figure 6.3 shows the estimates of relative expenditure per head based on the revised Arbuthnott adjustments for demography, morbidity and life circumstances, and remoteness.

- Under the revised proposals, expenditure per head on GMS would be relatively high in Health Boards with remote and rural populations - reflecting the substantial adjustment proposed for the effects of remoteness on the costs of providing GMS.

- Comparing Boards with similar levels of urbanity/rurality (e.g. Greater Glasgow and Lothian), Boards with relatively high levels of deprivation tend to have higher recommended expenditure levels per head.

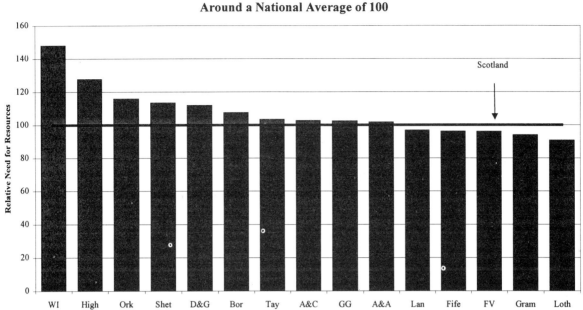

Figure 6.3: Overall Impact of the General Medical Services Model Around a National Average of 100

Note: these adjustments are around a national adjustment of zero

6.22   Table 6.2 compares each Health Board's current share of GMS resources with the target shares implied by the proposed Arbuthnott formula.

Table 6.2: Current and Target Shares of General Medical Services (Cash Limited and Non Cash Limited)

Health Board	Current Allocation Share %	New Allocation Share %	Change in Share %
Scotland	100.00	100.00	0.0
Argyll & Clyde	8.35	8.37	0.3
Ayrshire & Arran	6.96	7.39	6.1
Borders	2.22	2.17	-2.5
Dumfries & Galloway	3.21	3.19	-0.8
Fife	6.17	6.37	3.2
Forth Valley	4.87	5.22	7.2
Grampian	10.18	9.51	-6.5
Greater Glasgow	17.97	18.70	4.0
Highland	5.58	5.15	-7.7
Lanarkshire	9.50	10.50	10.5
Lothian	14.68	13.88	-5.4
Orkney	0.60	0.43	-28.6
Shetland	0.59	0.48	-19.8
Tayside	8.09	7.85	-2.9
Western Isles	1.02	0.79	-22.7

Note: the current share is based on the allocations to Health Boards for General Medical Services in 2000-01.
Any discrepancies are due to rounding.

STEERING GROUP RECOMMENDATIONS FOR GMS

6.23   The Steering Group consider that a basis has now been established on which a start can be made to implement a formula for allocating GMS resources. The analysis that has been done shows that the factors that influence relative healthcare needs in Hospital and Community Health Services and GP prescribing also influence the relative need for GMS. The pattern of relative needs for GMS resources between Health Boards is broadly similar to the pattern found in other services.

6.24   The remit that was set for this review does not cover issues about the implementation of a resource allocation formula. However, the Steering Group is conscious that some of the comments raised during consultation on *Fair Shares for All* reflected concerns about the how a GMS formula would be implemented.

6.25   The first point to note is that the implications of the changes in each Board's share of resources in Table 6.2 for actual expenditure levels on GMS will depend on a range of factors including, for example, the growth in total expenditure on GMS and the pace of change towards the new allocation shares.

6.26   Second, the Steering Group is also conscious of the concerns that were raised during consultation about the range and quality of the data available on GMS. While the Group is satisfied that the data provides a sound basis on which to begin implementing a needs-based allocation formula, it also considers it important that efforts should be made to improve this data so that the analysis of the relative needs for GMS resources can be developed further.

6.27   Third, there are important practical issues about the method of implementing changes in the distribution of GMS resources which will also need to be considered. For example, this will include the current split of resources between cash limited and non-cash limited.

CHAPTER 7:
UPDATING THE FORMULA

7.1   During consultation on *Fair Shares for All* a number of questions were asked about the arrangements for updating the proposed allocation formula. This chapter sets out the Steering Group's recommendations for updating the formula.

7.2   A resource allocation formula should be responsive to changing circumstances which will affect the relative needs of different Health Boards, though it also has to provide a reasonable measure of stability. Stability is also influenced, of course, by the pace at which progress is made towards target shares.

7.3   The formula has 4 basic components and the scope for updating needs to be considered in relation to each component:

- Health Board population shares;
- the adjustment for age and sex;
- the adjustment for morbidity and life circumstances;
- the adjustment for remoteness.

POPULATION SHARES

7.4   The Steering Group's recommendation is that Health Board population shares should be based on the Mid-Year Estimates of Population provided by the General Register Office for Scotland (GROS). These figures are produced each year by GROS and it would be appropriate to update the allocation formula to take account of changes in population estimates. The SHARE formula, including the population figures, has been frozen since this review of the allocation formula started in 1997-98. As a result significant changes have taken place in population shares over the last 2-3 years which have not been reflected in the allocation formula. It is particularly important to update population estimates as even over a relatively short space of time significant changes can take place in Health Board population shares. Annual updating of these figures will help to avoid the sharp discontinuities in target allocations that can occur if population shares are only revised every few years.

POPULATION AGE AND SEX

7.5   Estimates of the influence of age and sex on healthcare needs is based on the population estimates and information about the use of health services and their costs. Annual data are available on the use of services and their costs as well as the population estimates (by age and sex). It would therefore be possible to update the adjustment for age and sex each year, and the Steering Group recommend that this should be done. This, together with annual updating of the population count, would ensure a relatively smooth and gradual updating of the formula to reflect demographic changes.

MORBIDITY AND LIFE CIRCUMSTANCES

7.6   The 'Arbuthnott index' consists of four indicators. Three of these indicators are annually updateable: the mortality rate among people under 65, the unemployment rate, and the proportion of people over 65 claiming income support. The fourth indicator - households with two or more indicators of deprivation - is taken from the 1991 census and cannot be updated annually. It is important that a resource allocation formula should be responsive to changing socio-economic circumstances and the Steering Group recommends that the 'Arbuthnott index' should be re-calculated each year to reflect changes in the updateable indicators.

7.7   The influence of the 'Arbuthnott index' on Health Boards' relative need for healthcare also depends on statistical estimates of the relationship between this index and the use of services. The Steering Group does not consider that it is necessary or appropriate to re-estimate this relationship each year. The underlying relationship between indicators of need and the use of health services should be relatively stable from one year to another, and it should only be necessary to revise this estimate every few years. To review this relationship each year risks introducing an unnecessary element of instability into the formula. Our recommendation therefore is that the 'Arbuthnott index' should be updated each year and applied through the formula, but that statistical analysis of the relationship between this index and the use of services should only be re-estimated every few years.

7.8   The overall adjustment for morbidity and life circumstances is also influenced by the proportion of expenditure on different care programmes. As these proportions change over time as a result of changing patterns of care - e.g. the shift from hospital care into the community - it would seem appropriate to update the figures on the share of expenditure on different care programmes each year.

REMOTENESS

7.9   Estimates of the effects of remoteness on hospital services are based on the relationship between a broad indicator of remoteness (road kilometres per 1,000 population) and the relative costs of hospital services for the residents in different Heath Boards. There are two possible ways in which this adjustment could be updated.

- First, the estimates of road kilometres per head of population could be updated each year.
- Second, the underlying relationship between this indicator and the relative costs of hospital services in different Health Boards could also be re-estimated with additional data that becomes available each year.

7.10   The Steering Group does not consider that it would be appropriate to update the figures for road kilometres per 1,000 population or to re-estimate the relationship between this indicator and the costs of hospital services each year. The proposed adjustment for the effects of remoteness on the costs to Health Boards of securing hospital services for their residents is based on an estimate of the relationship between this indicator and costs using data for the last 3 years. We think that this adjustment should remain stable while further work is carried out on the implications of remoteness for the costs of hospital care.

7.11   The estimates of the effects of remoteness on community health services was based on a detailed study and it would not be possible to update this estimate without carrying out a further special study. Again, it would seem appropriate to continue to use this estimate while further work is done on the implications of remoteness for the costs of providing community health services.

CONCLUSIONS

7.12   A resource allocation formula should provide a reasonable measure of stability while being responsive to changes in the circumstances that influence the relative need for healthcare resources. A formula which is updated each year to take account of:

- changes in Health Board population shares (based on the annually updated Mid-Year Estimates);
- changes in the age and sex structure of the population;
- changes in the indicators of morbidity and life circumstances; and
- changes in the proportion of expenditure on different care programmes;

should provide an appropriate level of responsiveness.

ANNEX A:
CONTRIBUTION TO THE CONSULTATION OF THE NATIONAL REVIEW OF RESOURCE ALLOCATION

HEALTH BOARDS

Argyll & Clyde Health Board
Ayrshire and Arran Health Board
Borders Health Board
Dumfries & Galloway Health Board
Fife Health Board
Forth Valley Health Board
Grampian Health Board
Greater Glasgow Health Board
Highland Health Board
Lanarkshire Health Board
Lothian Health Board
Orkney Health Board
Shetland Health Board
Tayside Health Board
Western Isles Health Board

NHS TRUSTS

Ayrshire And Arran Primary Care Trust
Borders Community Health Services NHS Trust
Borders Primary Care NHS Trust
Dumfries & Galloway Primary Care NHS Trust
Fife Primary Care NHS Trust
Forth Valley Primary Care NHS Trust
Grampian Primary Care NHS Trust
Grampian University Hospitals NHS Trust
Highland Primary Care NHS Trust
Highland Acute Hospitals NHS Trust
Lanarkshire Acute Hospitals NHS Trust
Lanarkshire Primary Care NHS Trust
Lomond and Argyll Primary Care NHS Trust
Lothian University Hospitals NHS Trust
North Glasgow University Hospitals NHS Trust
Renfrewshire & Inverclyde Primary Care NHS Trust
South Glasgow University Hospitals NHS Trust
Tayside Primary Care NHS Trust
Tayside University Hospitals NHS Trust
Yorkhill NHS Trust

OTHERS

Dr N J Anderson (LMC)
Argyll & Bute Local Health Care Co-operative
Argyll and Clyde Local Health Council
Argyll and Clyde Local Medical Committee (General Practice)
Ayrshire and Arran Health Council
BMA Scottish Office (Scottish General Practitioners Committee)
British Medical Association Scottish Office Scotland
Mr Ewen Cameron
Capability Scotland
Ms Vera Carstairs
Chief Dental Officer, National Assembly for Wales
Community Council of The Royal Burgh of Peebles and District
Councillor Kingsley Thomas, City of Edinburgh Council
East Ayrshire Council
Fife Health Council
Fife Local Medical Committee (General Practice)
General Practitioners Sub-Committee of Lothian Area Medical Committee
Dr T C Gilhooly
Grampian Local Health Council
Grampian Local Medical Committee
Greater Glasgow Area Pharmaceutical Committee
Greater Glasgow Health Council
Mr L Gruer
Health Service Forum South East
Highland Health Council
Highland Users Group
Laurancekirk Medical Centre
Lothian Health Council
Dr D R Love
George Lyon MSP for Argyll and Bute
Macmillan Cancer Relief
National Asthma Campaign Scotland
Office for Public Health in Scotland
Orkney Local Health Council
Royal College of Midwives Scottish Board
Royal College of Nursing Scottish Board
Royal College of Physicians
Royal College of Surgeons of Edinburgh
Scottish Association of Health Councils
Scottish Drugs Forum
Scottish Medical Practices Committee
Scottish Parliament, Health and Community Care Committee
Shetland Local Health Council
Shore Street Dental Surgery
South Lanarkshire Council
Tayside Police

The British Psychological Society
The Chartered Society of Physiotherapy
The Surgery 'Geirhilda', Islay
Turning Point Scotland
Uist and Barra Health Council
University of Aberdeen, Department of General Practice and Primary Care
University of Glasgow, Department of General Practice
Ms R E Wallace (Common Services Agency)
West Lothian Council
Western Isles Local Medical Committee

ANNEX B:
LIST OF MEMBERSHIP OF GROUPS

STEERING GROUP

Professor Sir John Arbuthnott (Chairman)	Principal and Vice-Chancellor, University of Strathclyde
Mr John Aldridge	Director of Finance, Scottish Executive Health Department
Professor John Bain	Professor of General Practice, University of Dundee
Mr David Bolton	Director of Primary Care, Lothian Primary Care NHS Trust
Dr Adam Bryson	Medical Director, National Services Division, Common Services Agency
Mr Richard Copland	Director, Information and Statistics Division, Common Services Agency
Mr Stevan Croasdale (Secretary)	Assistant Statistician, Economics and Information Division, Scottish Executive Health Department
Mrs Kay Eastwood	Director of Nursing Services, Lomond and Argyll Primary Care NHS Trust
Dr Francis Elliot	Medical Director, Fife Primary Care NHS Trust
Mr David Hird	General Manager, Forth Valley Health Board
Professor Gavin McCrone	Vice-Chairman, Lothian University Hospitals NHS Trust
Dr Callum MacCleod	Chairman, Grampian Health Board
Ms Fiona Mackenzie	Chief Executive, Highland Primary Care NHS Trust
Mr Alasdair Munro	Head of Economics and Information Division, Scottish Executive Health Department
Mrs Agnes Robson	Director of Primary Care, Scottish Executive Health Department
Mr Matthew Sutton	Economic Adviser, Economics and Information Division, Scottish Executive Health Department
Dr Kevin Woods	Director of Strategy and Performance Management, Scottish Executive Health Department
Dr Lesley Wilkie	Director of Public Health, Argyll and Clyde Health Board
Mrs Julie Wilson	Senior Statistician, Economics and Information Division, Scottish Executive Health Department

REFERENCE GROUP

Mr Alasdair Munro .... Head of Economics and Information Division,
(Chairman)   Scottish Executive Health Department

Mrs Jennifer Bishop .... Statistician, Information and Statistics Division

Ms Vera Carstairs .... Research Consultant

Mr Neil Craig .... Lecturer, Department of Public Health, University of
                                                 Glasgow

Mr Stevan Croasdale .... Assistant Statistician, Economics and
(Secretary)   Information Division, Scottish Executive Health
                                                 Department

Dr Alastair Leyland .... Research Fellow, MRC Social and Public Health
                                                 Sciences Unit, University of Glasgow

Mr Mike Muirhead .... Statistician, Information and Statistics Division

Dr David Parkin .... Senior Lecturer, Department of Epidemiology and
                                                 Public Health, University of Newcastle-upon-Tyne

Mr Matthew Sutton .... Economic Advisor, Economics and Information
                                                 Division, Scottish Executive Health Mr

Mrs Julie Wilson .... Senior Statistician, Economics and Information
                                                 Division, Scottish Executive Health Department

WITH SPECIALIST INPUT FROM:

Mr Garnett Compton .... General Register Office for Scotland

Dr Philip McLoone .... Research Fellow, MRC Social and Public Health
                                                 Sciences Unit, University of Glasgow

Mr Peter Lock .... Ayrshire and Arran Health Board

Mr Frank Thomas .... General Register Office for Scotland

GMS SUB GROUP

Mr Alasdair Munro (Chairman)	Head of Economics and Information Division, Scottish Executive Health Department
Mr Matthew Armstrong	Primary Care Unit, Information and Statistics Division
Dr Colin Brown	Scottish General Practitioners Committee
Miss Susan Burney	Primary Care Unit, Information and Statistics Division
Dr A Gunning	Chief Executive, Ayrshire and Arran Primary Care NHS Trust
Dr K A Harden	Scottish General Practitioners Committee
Ms Kathy Jenkins	Scottish General Practitioners Committee
Mr Gavin Lewis (Secretary)	Economic Assistant, Economics and Information Division, Scottish Executive Health Department
Dr D R Love	Scottish General Practitioners Committee
Mr Tom Macdonald	Primary Care Directorate, Scottish Executive Health Department
Ms K M Matthew	Scottish General Practitioners Committee
Dr Anthony Scott	Senior Research Fellow, Health Economics Research Unit, Department of Public Health, University Medical Buildings, Foresterhill, Aberdeen
Mr Matthew Sutton	Economic Advisor, Economics and Information Division, Scottish Executive Health Department
Dr M Taylor	Department of General Practice and Primary Care, Foresterhill Health Centre
Dr J C Tiarks	Scottish General Practitioners Committee
Professor Graham Watt	Department of General Practice, University of Glasgow
Dr Hugh Whyte	Senior Medical Officer, Scottish Executive Health Department

ANNEX C:
THE CHOICE OF POPULATION COUNT

C.1   The choice of the population count for revenue allocations is a fundamental one. As explained in *Fair Shares for All* there were three different populations counts available at the time of conducting the Review:-

- the Community Health Index (CHI)– a listing of all patients registered with a GP
- the Mid-Year Estimates of Population (MYEs) produced by the General Register Office for Scotland (GROS)
- the Population Projections, also produced by GROS

C.2   As the CHI suffers from differential levels of "list size inflation", largely due to delays in de-registering patients that have left the practice or have died, this was ruled out as a data source for this purpose. The choice, therefore, was between the MYEs and the Projections. This annex provides more background information as to why the MYEs were recommended as the best choice of population count for the purpose of revenue allocations for Health, and further considers the analytical evidence in support of this recommendation.

ADVICE FROM GROS ON THE POPULATION COUNT

C.3   There are a number of reasons why GROS advise that theoretically the MYEs provide a more accurate reflection of the true population distribution within Scotland. The main reasons are:-

- The Estimates are derived from evidence about population changes within Scotland. The Projections however, are derived from assumptions based upon **past trends** in fertility, mortality and migration. They are not forecasts, they simply show what would happen if the assumptions were actually realised. A change in the magnitude or the direction of the trend will significantly affect the projected population. Therefore the MYE tends to provide the most up to date and accurate assessment of the relative shares of population for each Health Board.
- Given the use of MYEs as the base for the Projections, any uncertainties contained in the MYE will be automatically carried forward into the Projections. The MYEs are produced annually and therefore have the opportunity for improvement each year, whereas the Projections are generally updated every two years - so for one year out of every two, the most up to date information on population will not be used.
- In the context of year on year stability for revenue allocations, the MYEs provide a much more stable series. The Projections experience larger shifts (up and down) in the year on year population count being projected than the MYE due to the production of Projections with a new base population and assumptions every other year.

ANALYSIS OF RECENT TRENDS IN POPULATION DATA

C.4   The use of the population count in revenue allocations is to determine the relative population share each Health Board has of the Scotland total – so the accuracy of the relative shares is more important than the absolute count. Ideally, it would be best to use the MYE for the corresponding financial year, as it would be the most accurate estimate of each Health Board's share of the total population of Scotland. So for the 2000-01 allocations our "actual MYE" would be the 2000 MYE. However, the allocations require to be run before the financial year begins, whilst MYEs are published around the end of the financial year – so this is not possible.

C.5   The practicalities of timing are such that there is a choice between using the latest available MYE (which relates to two years before the financial year of interest) or the latest available Projection (which was produced one or two years earlier but projects forward to the financial year of interest). For example, we would wish to run the allocations for 2000-01 in the autumn of 1999. At that point in time, the choice would be between the 1998 MYE and the 1996-based projection for the mid-year 2000. In judging the merits of the MYE against the Projection it is possible to compare these two options against the 2000 MYE once it becomes available – which was the basis for our work.

C.6   In order to assess the merits of each of the two sources of population counts for revenue allocations for Health we considered a number of different aspects. The evidence shows the MYEs are more suitable than the Projections in relation to five key issues of accuracy and stability described below. Table 1 summarises how different the Health Board shares from the older MYE and from the Projection were from the MYE for the year of the allocations (referred to as the 'actual MYE'), by Health Board, for each of the latest six years. The tables shows the 'mean squared error' of each source compared with the "actual MYE", with the figures multiplied by 10,000 for ease of reading the scale. The mean squared error is simply a measure of how different one way of measuring the Health Board's share of population is from the 'actual MYE'. This allows us to assess accuracy in terms of: how frequently one source performed better; for each Health Board which source was more accurate; and for each year which source was more accurate.

C.7   Each of these issues relates to 'what was most frequently accurate?', however it is also important to consider the magnitude of the overall error in each source. Table 2 illustrates this point, by summarising how much of the overall population share do we consider was inaccurately allocated. Given that the population count is the main driver of the allocations, the other key aspect is the year on year stability of each source. Table 3 illustrates this by summarising the annual absolute change in the population count for each Board – with large changes being less desirable. Each table shows the more accurate or more stable figure in bold.

It is helpful to consider the results in these tables in terms of a series of questions about accuracy and stability:-

i   How frequently did the MYE or the Projection give a more accurate reflection of the Health Board's actual population share?

Table 1 shows that in 61 out of the 90 individual comparisons, the MYE was more accurate.

ii   For each individual Health Board over the six years, how close overall were the MYEs and the Projections to the actual Health Board shares?

Table 1 shows that, with the exception of Argyll & Clyde where the overall results for the six years was almost identical, the MYEs were more accurate for all Health Boards.

iii   For Scotland as a whole for a given year, did the MYE provide more accurate shares of population overall than the Projection?

Table 1 shows that for each of the six years, the MYEs were more accurate for Scotland as a whole than the Projections.

iv   For Scotland as a whole for a given year, what share of the overall population was not accurately allocated to Health Boards?

Table 2 shows that for the latest five years, the MYE gave a more accurate distribution of the total population of Scotland than the Projections.

v   In terms of year on year stability, does the MYE or the Projection provide a more stable series?

Table 3 summarises the year on year volatility of the Health Board shares for each data source. In every Health Board the MYEs were more stable year on year than the Projections.

Table 1: Assessment of the Accuracy of the Available MYE and Projection Against the "Actual MYE" for the Financial Year of Interest. (mean squared error * 10,000)

Health Board	Population Source	Financial Year of Allocation						Six Year Average
		93-94	94-95	95-96	96-97	97-98	98-99	
Scotland	MYE	**0.80**	**0.35**	**0.41**	**0.42**	**0.72**	**1.01**	
	Projection	1.69	3.34	4.19	0.49	1.32	1.61	
Argyll & Clyde	MYE	**1.35**	0.51	**0.12**	0.24	0.29	0.47	0.50
	Projection	2.31	**0.01**	0.21	**0.02**	**0.09**	**0.35**	0.50
Ayrshire & Arran	MYE	0.16	**0.10**	**0.05**	**0.00**	0.01	0.02	**0.05**
	Projection	**0.00**	1.81	2.40	0.01	**0.00**	**0.00**	0.70
Borders	MYE	0.56	**0.19**	**0.28**	0.21	0.08	**0.12**	**0.24**
	Projection	**0.12**	2.81	3.82	**0.00**	**0.00**	0.16	1.15
Dumfries & Galloway	MYE	**0.11**	0.23	0.10	0.00	**0.02**	0.00	**0.08**
	Projection	1.53	**0.02**	**0.00**	0.06	0.20	0.03	0.31
Fife	MYE	0.90	**0.05**	**0.04**	**0.51**	**0.41**	0.00	**0.32**
	Projection	**0.05**	2.26	1.52	1.14	2.02	0.06	1.18
Forth Valley	MYE	**0.13**	**0.02**	**0.00**	0.27	0.79	**0.35**	**0.26**
	Projection	0.44	0.41	0.61	**0.17**	**0.50**	0.42	0.43
Grampian	MYE	**4.88**	**2.22**	**0.32**	**0.03**	**0.31**	0.97	**1.45**
	Projection	7.49	19.87	18.60	1.55	4.12	3.52	9.19
Greater Glasgow	MYE	1.18	**0.35**	**0.45**	0.47	**0.29**	**0.11**	**0.48**
	Projection	**0.02**	2.98	3.54	**0.41**	0.58	2.25	1.63
Highland	MYE	0.84	**0.13**	**0.13**	0.44	**0.17**	**0.00**	**0.28**
	Projection	**0.00**	1.28	1.58	**0.15**	0.57	0.76	0.72
Lanarkshire	MYE	0.14	**0.24**	**0.13**	**0.00**	**0.12**	**0.02**	**0.11**
	Projection	**0.06**	1.36	2.13	0.02	0.32	0.38	0.71
Lothian	MYE	**0.00**	**0.41**	**1.17**	1.65	1.51	0.84	**0.93**
	Projection	0.04	2.01	4.13	**0.74**	**1.48**	**0.13**	1.42
Orkney	MYE	0.27	**0.01**	**0.06**	**0.00**	**0.02**	1.26	**0.27**
	Projection	**0.13**	3.21	4.67	1.80	1.86	6.39	3.01
Shetland	MYE	**1.11**	**0.41**	**0.66**	0.48	**0.00**	**0.10**	**0.46**
	Projection	1.67	6.19	10.17	**0.32**	0.82	3.67	3.81
Tayside	MYE	0.20	**0.10**	**0.05**	0.07	**0.29**	**0.67**	**0.23**
	Projection	**0.02**	1.15	1.75	0.45	0.86	1.20	0.90
Western Isles	MYE	**0.19**	**0.30**	**2.56**	1.97	6.51	10.26	**3.63**
	Projection	11.49	4.71	7.68	**0.56**	**6.42**	**4.79**	5.94

Note: In this table a lower value for the mean squared error shows that one source of data was more Accurate than the other. These have been highlighted in bold text.

Table 2: Assessment of Total Population Misallocated

Year of Allocation	MYE	Projection
1993-94	0.394%	**0.312%**
1994-95	**0.291%**	0.357%
1995-96	**0.252%**	0.363%
1996-97	**0.261%**	0.293%
1997-98	**0.301%**	0.445%
1998-99	**0.256%**	0.425%

Note: For example this table shows that for 1998-99, 0.256% was misallocated using MYEs compared with 0.425% using projections.

Table 3: Assessment of Year on Year Stability of Each Source of Population Count, by Health Board

Health Board	MYE %	Projection %
Argyll & Clyde	0.36	0.57
Ayrshire & Arran	0.14	0.55
Borders	0.24	0.65
Dumfries & Galloway	0.12	0.29
Fife	0.29	0.68
Forth Valley	0.22	0.50
Grampian	0.57	1.25
Greater Glasgow	0.43	0.69
Highland	0.26	0.63
Lanarkshire	0.17	0.62
L̤ ̤ian	0.44	0.78
Orkney	0.38	1.00
Shetland	0.37	1.18
Tayside	0.29	0.63
Western Isles	0.80	0.97

Note: For example this table shows that on average, over the six years, the population share
for Argyll & Clyde changed by 0.36% per annum using MYEs, compared with 0.57% using Projections.

ANNEX D:
ADJUSTMENTS FOR AGE AND SEX

D.1   In *Fair Shares for All* estimates were made of the relative use of services by different age and sex groups in the population. The estimates for these population sub-groups were based on information about:

- the number of episodes per head of population in each sub-group;
- the lengths of stay in hospital; and
- the average costs of the services used.

This information takes into account differences between population sub-groups in the frequency with which services are used, differences in lengths of stay, and differences in the mix of specialties used.

D.2   A number of concerns were raised during consultation about this method of determining age/sex cost weights. In the main these concerns related to the method of calculating age/sex weights for acute hospital services.

- Differences in methods of recording patient activity among Trusts and Health Boards may influence the estimates. For example, in some areas it may be more common to transfer patients between specialties during the same period of treatment than in other areas. Thus the same treatment may be recorded as a single episode in one Health Board area while being recorded as two separate episodes in another Health Board area.
- Second, the basis on which some costs are treated as 'fixed' costs and others as 'variable' costs was questioned. Fixed costs are costs that are assumed to be the same for all patients treated in a specialty, while the variable costs is assumed to vary directly with the length of stay. Thus, elderly people who tend to have longer lengths of stay will therefore have a higher overall cost per case because of the increased variable element. It was assumed in *Fair Shares for All* that medical, theatre and laboratory costs are fixed, while all other costs such as nursing were assumed to be variable and were allocated in relation to length of stay. This reflected a judgement about which costs were most closely linked to the number of patients treated and which were most closely linked to the number of bed days.
- The cost data used in this analysis were drawn from Health Service Costs (the Blue Book), and included the costs of teaching hospitals. These costs reflect the influence of a range of factors including the costs associated with teaching responsibilities. It was suggested during consultation that this may distort the results since the additional costs of teaching (ACT) are not covered by the resource allocation formula.

D.3   In response to these concerns a number of alternative methods of estimating age/sex cost weights have been examined and the results of these alternatives have been compared. In total 5 alternative methods were considered for costing inpatient activity (day cases are always costed on the basis of cost per case).

71

(a) This method modifies the approach in *Fair Shares for All* by only applying a fixed cost to certain episodes. Fixed costs were not applied to the following episodes:

- transfers which represent a return to a specialty in which a patient has formerly been treated within the same continuous inpatient stay; and
- transfers of emergency medical admissions within the first 48 hours only if transferred to another medical specialty.

(b) This option is the same approach adopted in *Fair Shares for All*. A fixed cost is applied to all recorded SMR1 episodes of activity, and a variable cost per day is applied to the length of stay. The split of costs into fixed and variable categories is the same as in *Fair Shares for All*.

(c) This method assumes that all costs are proportional to length of stay and therefore a uniform cost per day is applied to all episodes within a specialty.

(d) This option takes a different approach to the method of determining the split between fixed and variable costs. Estimates of the split are based on regression analysis of the relationship between average length of stay and cost per case in different hospitals. These fixed costs are only applied to episodes satisfying specified criteria (i.e. excluding the cases listed in (a).

(e) This method also uses regression analysis to determine the split between fixed and variable costs. However teaching hospitals have been excluded from the estimates. These fixed costs are only applied to episodes satisfying specified criteria (i.e. excluding the cases listed in (a).

D.4   These methods have been used to calculate the relative age/sex cost weights for different population subgroups. The results are shown in Table D.1 and in Figures D.1 and D.2.

Table D.1: Acute Costs per Head of Population (Inpatient and Day Cases only), 1996-97

Option: Inpatients costed as	Sex	Cost per Head (£) by Age Band							
		0-4	5-14	15-24	25-44	45-64	65-74	75-84	85+
a) Fixed and Variable	male	292	79	81	106	281	678	1,122	1,752
	female	223	65	81	129	248	528	945	1,597
b) Fixed (applied to all episodes) and Variable	male	292	78	80	105	281	680	1,125	1,754
	female	223	64	81	128	247	529	947	1,600
c) Cost per day	male	282	67	67	94	278	704	1,181	1,848
	female	215	57	68	117	248	558	1,011	1,714
d) Fixed and Variable derived from regression	male	296	81	85	110	282	670	1,096	1,702
	female	225	66	87	132	248	520	922	1,562
e) Fixed and Variable excludes Teaching costs derived from regression	male	290	81	85	111	286	678	1,096	1,686
	female	222	66	86	131	248	521	918	1,553

D.5   All 5 options produce very similar estimates of the *relative* expenditure per head of population within each age group for both males and females. The option which differs most from the others is Option C which assumes that all costs are variable and applies a uniform variable cost per day to all acute activity. This produces higher estimates of average expenditure per head among the older age groups than the other options because it effectively assumes that a stay in hospital of 10 days costs twice as much as a stay of 5 days. This seems an extreme assumption, and it would be more realistic to assume that some element of costs are fixed and are common to all admissions within a specialty while other costs vary with length of stay.

Figure D.1: Age/Sex Cost Curves
Males 1996-97

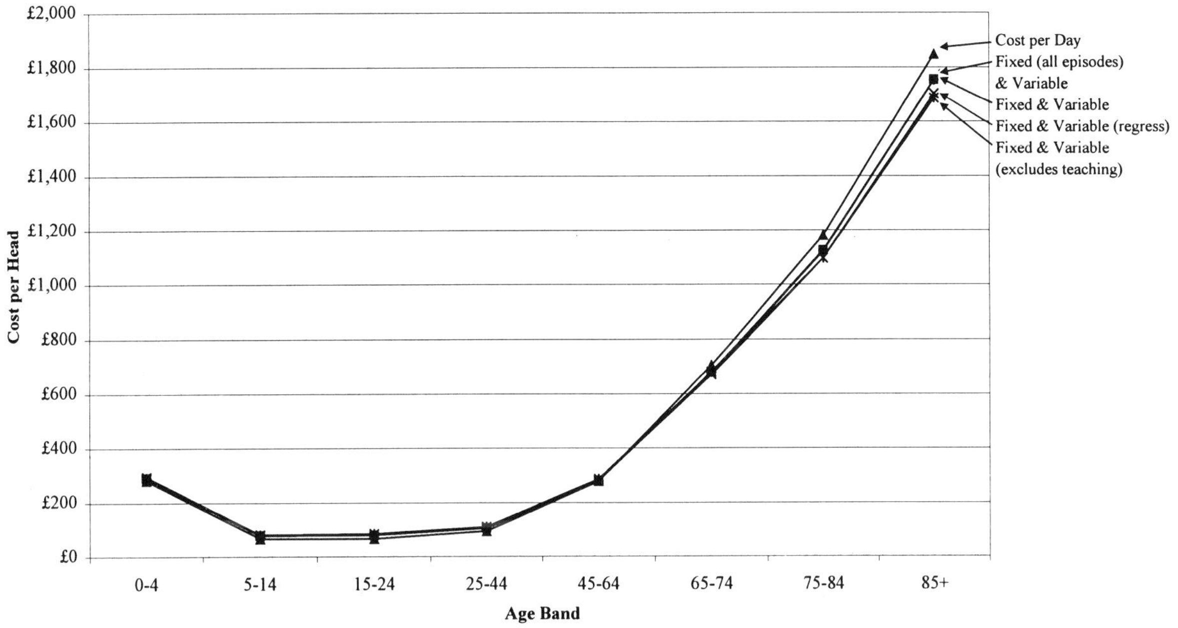

Figure D.2: Age/Sex Cost Curves
Females 1996-97

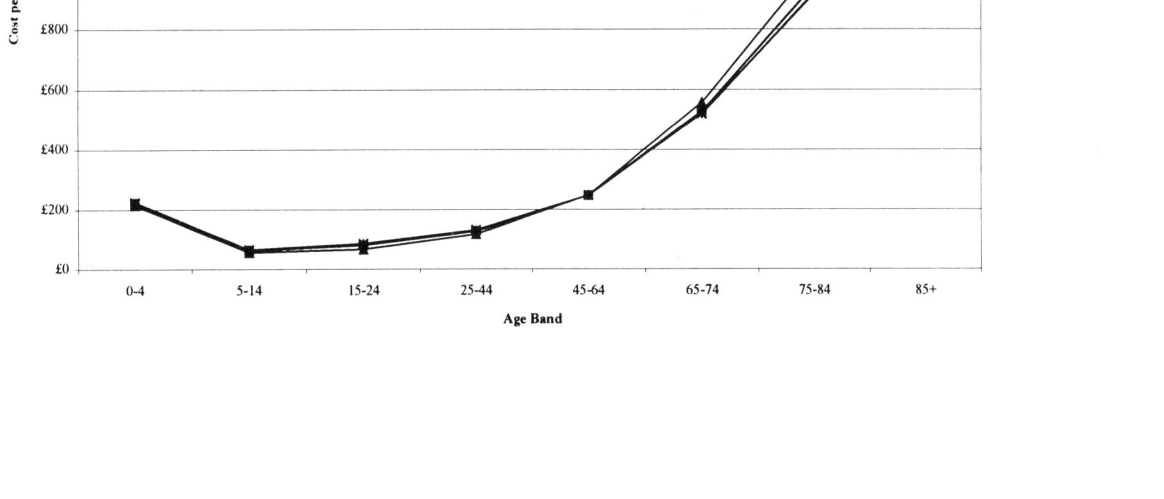

D.6   There is very little to choose between the other methods of calculating age/sex weights in the acute specialties.

- A comparison of Options (a) and (b) suggest that changes in the method of calculating inpatient activity has a negligible effect on the relative cost weights among population sub-groups.

- A comparison between Options (d) and (e) suggest that it makes very little difference whether the additional costs associated with teaching are included or excluded when estimating *relative* age/sex cost weights. At first sight this may seem surprising. However, it should be borne in mind that in calculating the *relative* cost weights by population sub-group the purpose is to identify to what extent expenditure per head in each sub-group is above or below the national average. Total expenditure per head with teaching costs included will be higher, but the evidence suggests that this has a very small effect on *relative* expenditure per head. (It is also worth noting that in each option, total expenditure on acute services has been scale back to the same figure to ensure that the options are comparable.)

D.7   Given the close similarity of the results for nearly all of these options, the choice will have very little effect on allocations between Health Boards. In the end it has been decided to adopt Option (d) for the following reasons.

- It is relatively straightforward to apply since it is based on recorded SMR episodes and Blue Book cost data.

- It is based on evidence of the split between fixed and variable costs unlike the methods used in Options (a) and (b) which rely on rather arbitrary judgements about whether a particular category of cost should be treated as 'fixed' or 'variable'.

D.8   There are a few other points to note about this method of determining the age/sex cost weights for acute specialties. First, some Health Boards were concerned that the adjustment to take account of the age and sex structure of their population would be influenced by the pattern of services locally. It was suggested for example that Boards that carry out a relatively high proportion of day case activity may be disadvantaged because estimates of the costs per head of population in their areas will be lower as a result. As explained earlier the estimates of age/sex weights are based on *national* patterns of activity (and costs) by population sub-group which are then applied to each Health Board's population structure. Differences in patterns of patient activity among Boards will not influence the adjustment that is applied to take account of local demography.

D.9   A related concern was that Boards that are relatively efficient and have relatively low costs per case may also be penalised because they will be given a lower weighting in the adjustment for age/sex than other Boards. Again, it is important to recognise that this adjustment is based on *national* cost rates. The adjustment applied to each Board is not influenced by differences in the efficiency with which services are provided.

D.10   The use of Blue Book cost data that include teaching costs (as well as other provider subsidies) raised concerns that all of these costs would now be allocated through a general formula, and this would lead to a redistribution of ACT money away from teaching to non-teaching Health Boards. However ACT funding will continue to be allocated separately from the general formula covered in this review. Blue Book cost data are used to estimate the *relative* costs of treating patients from different population sub-groups. The evidence of Table

D.1 above shows that it makes no material difference to these estimates of *relative* expenditure per head of population whether teaching costs are included or excluded.

D.11 Finally, it was suggested during consultation that the results of the expenditure per head estimates for the older age groups were surprising because they show that expenditure per head is higher in males than in females. This was thought to be at odds with evidence that women account for a relatively high proportion of acute admissions in the older age groups. It is important however to distinguish between *expenditure per head* and *total expenditure* on male and female subgroups. Women account for a significantly higher proportion of the population in the older age groups and, although average expenditure per head on women may be lower than on men, this is more than offset by the greater number of women in these age bands.

D.12 The following table shows the cost curves used for the 1997-98 analyses (note these cover inpatient, day case and outpatient activity). Acute and maternity were costed as described above. Mental illness, care of the elderly and people with learning disabilities are now based on specialty specific cost per day (as the majority of cases are variable). Further work has been carried out on prescribing to ensure consistency of approach with other care programmes.

Table D.2: Cost per Head by Age Group for HCHS 1997-98

	Sex	Cost per Head by Age Group (£s)							
		0-4	5-14	15-24	25-44	45-64	65-74	75-84	85+
Acute	male	370.53	130.42	120.28	154.31	349.23	782.06	1,210.35	1,803.31
	Female	294.47	115.82	134.48	188.59	329.63	628.76	1,042.50	1,691.89
Mental Illness	male	1.96	9.55	33.01	53.26	59.10	129.71	294.37	529.60
	female	0.72	7.56	22.79	36.02	45.15	113.32	289.54	583.87
Care of the Elderly	male	0.00	0.00	0.11	0.47	5.05	61.85	236.87	660.97
	female	0.00	0.00	0.12	0.47	3.99	52.75	273.78	1,045.19
Learning Disabilities	male	0.45	0.82	7.88	36.01	32.76	20.99	22.22	13.61
	female	0.36	0.87	4.90	21.62	25.62	17.28	15.80	9.48
Community	male	115.47	58.10	58.31	58.00	55.68	81.08	189.02	197.24
	female	114.39	55.92	68.27	67.90	54.82	81.61	191.35	197.29

		Cost Per Birth by Mother's Age Group (£s)							
		-	15-19	20-24	25-29	30-34	35-39	40-44	45-49
Maternity	female		2,706.38	2,419.08	2,230.17	2,146.71	2,299.37	2,727.17	3,623.42

		Cost per Head by Age Group (£s)								
		0-4	5-15	16-24	25-44	45-59	60-64	65-75	75+	Temp Res
Prescribing	male	16.64	29.72	28.19	64.29	137.69	137.69	249.54	296.33	8.47
	female	20.35	17.13	50.24	81.27	158.54	221.51	245.81	262.40	8.47

ANNEX E:
MORBIDITY AND LIFE CIRCUMSTANCES

E.1   A number of technical issues were raised during consultation about the method of estimating the influence of morbidity and life circumstances on the need for healthcare resources. These included:

- the use of small area analysis;
- the measurement of population at small area level;
- the measurement of supply;
- the year on year stability of these methods;
- community health services

SMALL AREA ANALYSIS

E.2   The analysis of the influence of morbidity and life circumstances in the first report on *Fair Shares for All* was based on information from 895 postcode sectors, which ranged in population size from 35 people to 19,579 with a mean of 5,730. In the regression analysis the data were population weighted to reduce the risk of small postcode sectors with extreme values exerting undue influence on the results. However some concerns were expressed during consultation that the presence of a significant number of sectors with relatively small populations could still have a distorting effect on the results.

E.3   A related issue concerns a slight mismatch between the small area definitions used in the indicators of morbidity and life circumstances drawn from the 1991 census and the indicators that are annually updateable. The indicators that can be updated annually are available down to postcode sector level. However the indicators taken from the 1991 Census Local Base Tables (LBS) are not available in the same detail. In the LBS tables census data are not released for postcode sectors with fewer than 1,000 persons or 320 households because of concerns about confidentiality. The data for these areas are included with the results for another appropriate sector. In addition where a postcode sector crosses a Local Authority boundary the postcode sector was split along this boundary, forming a part sector. This was added to its nearest neighbour within the same Authority, resulting in modified postcode sectors. The result of these adjustments to the census data is that in about 10% of postcode sectors there is some degree of mismatch with the areas for which the annually updateable indicators of morbidity and life circumstances are available. For some areas the census postcode sector may include data relating to a small neighbouring area whilst the non-census data for the same sector has not been modified in that way.

E.4   To address these issues the definition of postcode sectors has been reviewed and small postcode sectors have been amalgamated with neighbouring sectors to improve the robustness of the data. The amalgamation was carried out by grouping those part sectors that were amalgamated for census confidentiality reasons together to form groups of adjacent postcode sectors. This ensures that the areas covered by the re-defined postcode sectors in the census-based indicators of morbidity and life circumstances are consistent with the areas covered by the annually updateable indicators.

E.5   The result of this amalgamation process is that the number of postcode sectors used in the analysis has been reduced from 895 to 717, and the population size for each sector now ranges from 874 to 34,495 in 1996-97, with an average of 7,152. The following chart compares the size distribution of postcode sectors in the revised analysis with the distribution in the first report on *Fair Shares for All*. There are no longer any sectors with a population of fewer than 500, compared with 74 sectors in the earlier analysis. The number of sectors with a population between 500 and 1,000 has fallen from 37 to 2.

Figure E.1: Comparison of Postcode Sector Populations used in First and Final Reports; Number of Postcode Sectors Within Specified Population Bands (1996-97)

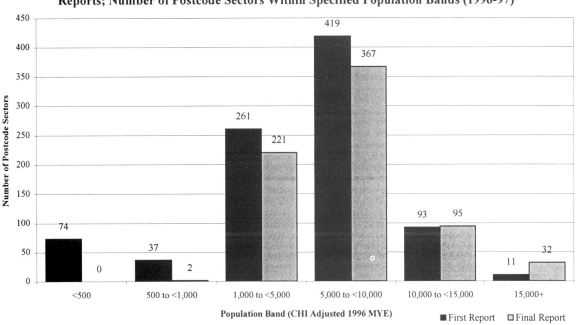

E.6   The reduction in the number of postcode sectors with relatively small populations reduces any risk that the results of the analysis of the influence of indicators of morbidity and life circumstances on the relative use of services might be affected by small numbers. However, further work has been done to check the possible influence of postcode sectors with relatively small populations on the regression results using 'shrinkage' techniques.

E.7   The rationale for shrinkage techniques is that the use of indicators of morbidity and life circumstances in the regression ignores any uncertainty that there is surrounding the estimate of a particular indicator in any particular postcode sector (the 'point estimate' for that sector). Although the point estimates are **accurate**, the confidence intervals around these estimates indicate that those based on larger postcode sectors are more **reliable**. The figures are 'accurate' in that they are based on enumeration not sampling and represent a snapshot of the areas as they were on census day in 1991. But the proportions will change as both enumerators and denominators change over time owing to changing populations (through birth, death, migration) and changing ownership of property. If the census had been conducted a week later then the figures would be different for some areas; we would expect these differences to be greater in areas with smaller populations. For example, the point estimate of the proportion of the population living in owner occupied accommodation in KA3 4 (which has 1,288 inhabitants) was 67.5% and for PH4 1 (which has 31,302 inhabitants) was 68.6%. Although fairly similar proportions are observed, the 95% confidence intervals around these estimates were 67.5% +/- 2.5% and 68.6% +/- 0.5% respectively. The confidence region around the smaller area is approximately 5 times that around the larger area.

E.8   The method of shrinkage estimates tries to take account of the differing degrees of reliability by considering how much evidence there is for the estimate for one postcode sector being different from an estimate in which there is more confidence – such as the national mean. A shrinkage estimator is essentially a weighted average of the value observed in an area and the mean – with the weights depending on the amount of information available in each area (e.g. the population size). So the larger the area's population the more weight is given to the point estimate for that area, whilst the smaller the area the more weight is given to the national mean – and hence the greater the "shrinkage" towards the national mean.

E.9   All of the indicators of morbidity and life circumstances available that had been used in the regression work were calculated as shrunken estimates – both to the national mean and to the Health Board level mean. The correlation between the original point estimates and the shrunken estimates can then be used to assess the potential impact of adopting the shrunken estimates instead. This work showed that for nearly all of the indicators of morbidity and life circumstances that had been considered in the review the correlation was over 95%. This work indicates that there is no evidence that more accurate Health Board adjustments would be obtained through the use of shrinkage estimators.

MEASUREMENT OF POPULATION AT SMALL AREA LEVEL

E.10   When the data was originally assembled for the Arbuthnott Review work was carried out to apply anonymised data from the Community Health Index (CHI) to the GROS Mid-Year Estimates (MYEs) of the population to obtain postcode sector level estimates of the population. Since that work was carried out GROS have set up their own Working Group to investigate the potential for using the CHI and MYEs to produce reliable small area population estimates for a range of users. In the post consultation period we were able to drawn on the progress made by that Working Group to make some improvements to our methodology. The main source of improvement made was to apply the CHI data to the Local Authority level MYE data rather than just Health Board level. Some Boards span several Local Authorities, so more accurate estimates were obtained by using the smaller units of geography – by scaling to 32 Local Authority totals rather than just 15 Health Boards.

MEASUREMENT OF SUPPLY

E.11   Estimates of the relationship between the use of services and indicators of morbidity and life circumstances take account of the influence of supply (or accessibility) on the use of services. Chapter 4 of the Technical Report to *Fair Shares for All* described the way in which accessibility was calculated. Essentially it is a distance weighted beds per head of population, with the key equation being:

$$A_i = \sum_d \left(\frac{B_d / (10 + d_{id}^2)}{\sum_i P_i / (10 + d_{id}^2)} \right)$$

where: A_i is the accessibility index for postcode sector i;

B_d is the number of relevant beds at hospital d;

d_{id} is the distance in km between centroid of postcode sector i and hospital d; and

P_i is the relevant population of postcode sector i.

E.12   Some concern was raised during the consultation as to whether the distance decay function of $1/(10 + d^2)$ was the most appropriate for Scotland. Commentators on this issue considered squaring the distance gave too sharp a reduction in access, and questioned the use of the constant of 10km (which was intended to prevent unrealistically high access scores in the immediate vicinity of facilities).

E.13   Further work was carried out using power functions other than distance squared (e.g. $1/d$) and using a range of exponential decay functions – to allow for a more gradual decline in the accessibility. In this work an evidence base was sought for the most suitable distance decay function to reflect the spatial arrangement of hospital beds in Scotland in relation to its population. The analytical work suggested that out of a range of power and exponential functions, the function

$$\exp^{-0.1*\text{distance}}$$

gave the best fit to the Scottish data as it minimised the coefficient of variation when regressed against the dependant variable for acute services. This was adopted for the post consultation modelling work.

E.14   Figure E.2 shows the more realistic gradual decay offered by the exponential function adopted when compared with 1/distance.

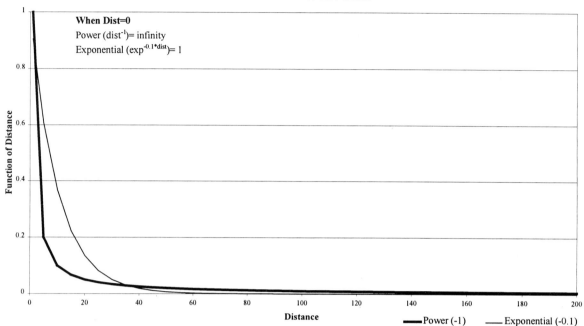

**Figure E.2: Power (dist^{-1}) and Exponential(exp$^{-0.1*dist}$) Functions
for Distance = 1 to 200 units**

E.15 It is important to note that for a number of sectors the impact of this choice between the most appropriate power function and the best performing exponential function was fairly negligible. This is shown in Figure E.3 below, where we see that for the bulk of the postcode sectors in Scotland the results are very similar. Given that we are limited to the measurement of straight line distances, the main improvement here is the use of an evidence base to make the selection of the most appropriate distance decay function for the geography of Scotland.

**Figure E.3: Final Access Scores Using Power (dist-1) and
Exponential (exp-0.1*dist) Functions, by Ranked Postcode Sectors**

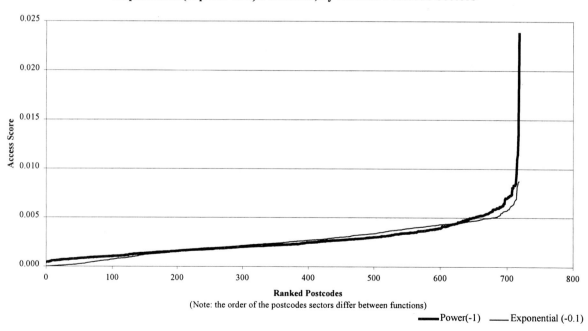

E.16   In *Fair Shares for All* the access measures used covered a number of types of hospital bed provision, local authority residential homes and private nursing homes – together with some measures relating only to the prescribing work (such as whether the practice was a dispensing practice).   In the post consultation work a range of other social work indicators relating to access to day care places and home help provision were also obtained and tested out in the modelling – to address any concerns about the model not picking up sufficient information on alternative provision.

YEAR ON YEAR STABILITY OF THE MODELS

E.17   In order to test the year on year stability the estimates of relative need based on the revised models applied to 1996-97 data were compared with estimates based on models applied to 1997-98 data.   The results showed that in some care programmes the estimates of relative need differed significantly between the 2 years which indicated some instability in the approach. Several possible causes of year on year stability problems were considered:

- the stability of the dependent variables;
- the stability of the independent variables;
- the stability of the relationship between the dependent and independent variables;
- the stability of the modelling approach.

E.18   There is high correlation between health service use at postcode sector level in 1996-97 and 1997-98 which suggests that the problem is not caused by instability in the dependent variable.

E.19   There are several reasons for assuming that the indicators of morbidity and life circumstances are also relatively stable over time. First, many of the indicators used in this analysis were taken from the 1991 census and do not change over time. Second, some of the updateable indicators such as the standardised mortality rates are based on five-year averages which will ensure a significant degree of year-on-year stability. Third, the indicators that are annually updateable show a high degree of stability over the 2 years. Finally, the significant reduction in the number of postcode sectors with relatively small populations should also contribute to greater stability in both the dependent and independent variables.

E.20   The third possible cause of instability is that the relationship between the dependent and independent variables - i.e. the relationship between deprivation and resource use - is itself subject to significant changes from year-to-year. Given that the relative needs for healthcare are influenced by an accumulation of social and economic circumstances, it seems very unlikely that the relationship between deprivation and resource use would be relatively unstable from one year to another. As a test of the stability of this relationship, the dependent variable was regressed against the Carstairs deprivation index (which does not change between census dates) in 1996-97 and 1997-98. The results showed that the difference between these two years in the estimated effect of the Carstairs index on use of services was very small and not statistically significant. This suggests that the relationship between patterns of service use and deprivation is stable.

E.21   The source of the instability seemed to lie in one aspect of the modelling approach: the use of a very large number of indicators of morbidity and life circumstances. Examination of the modelling results showed that the set of indicators of morbidity and life circumstances that were found to be statistically significant each year could be quite different. For example the table E.1 compares the indicators that were identified as statistically significant in the 1996-97 and 1997-98 models for Digestive Diseases. Although 9 indicators were identified as statistically significant in each year, the only indicator that is common to the models for both years is the proportion of people over 65 on income support.

Table E.1: Comparison of Indicators Identified as Significant for Digestive Diseases, 1996-97 and 1997-98

Needs Indicator	1996-97 Model	1997-98 Model
SMR0-64		✓
Mean Birthweight		✓
Long Term Unemployment	✓	
1991 Census Unemployment		✓
Unemployment Rate	✓	
Youth Unemployment	✓	
People Over 65 on Income Support	✓	✓
People Over 75 Living Alone	✓	
Dependents in Single Carer Households		✓
Manual Classes		✓
Social Classes 1 and 2		✓
Private and Public Renting	✓	
Overcrowded Households	✓	
People Moving from Outside the LA Area	✓	
South East Asian Households		✓
Households in Other Ethnic Groups	✓	
People with a Degree		✓

The results for Digestive Diseases provides a rather extreme example of the changes that could occur in the independent variables identified as statistically significant in models run separately on data for 1996-97 and 1997-98. In most care programmes and disease groups, the degree of change in the significant variables between the two years was less pronounced, though some changes would normally occur. Although many of these independent variables are quite highly correlated with each other, they are not so highly correlated that changes will have no effect on the estimates of relative need derived from these models.

E.22   Although reducing the number of indicators of morbidity and life circumstances in the analysis improved the stability of the models, it was felt that the scale of change from one year to another in the estimates of relative need by Health Board in some care programmes was higher than could be accepted. We also explored the potential of using principal component analysis to reduce the number of indicators of morbidity and life circumstances and thus minimise the problem of having such a large number of highly correlated indicators. However, this method, which attempts to identify underlying components that explain the pattern of correlations within a set of indicators, does not offer a definitive solution to the problem. Therefore we looked to the analytical evidence of the modelling as the means of identifying those key indicators of Morbidity and Life Circumstances that best explained the use of services. This small number of key indicators was then combined into a single index (the 'Arbuthnott index') of morbidity and life circumstances. The basis of this index is described in Annex F.

COMMUNITY HEALTH SERVICES

E.23   Community health services cover a wide range of different services and it is not possible to estimate the influence of morbidity and life circumstances on each service because of the limited data available. The only areas where it has been possible to do so are district nursing and health visiting, and in *Fair Shares for All* the combined relative needs index for these two services was applied to all community health services.

E.24   During consultation some concerns were expressed about this approach. It was suggested that it would be more appropriate to apply estimates of the effects of morbidity and life circumstances from other care programmes to these services. For example, the estimate of relative need for hospital maternity services could be applied to community midwifery services, and the relative needs index for GMS could be applied to clinic-based community services.

E.25   As noted in *Fair Shares for All* there is no clear evidence to support either of these alternative approaches. However, the weight of views expressed during consultation was that it would be better to use relative needs indices from other care programmes rather than to assume that the needs index for district nursing and health visiting can be applied throughout community services. Accordingly, the Steering Group agreed that the method used to estimate relative needs for community health services as a result of morbidity and life circumstances should be changed.

ANNEX F:
THE 'ARBUTHNOTT INDEX'

F.1   In the further analytical work that has been carried out following consultation on *Fair Shares for All* a large number of indicators was used to analyse the relationship between morbidity and life circumstances and the use made of different health services. Four indicators were found to be significantly more successful than other indicators in explaining the differences observed in the use of services between postcode areas. These indicators are:

- The standardised mortality rate among people aged 0-64 averaged over a 5 year period.
- The proportion of households having 2 or more deprivation indicators.
- The proportion of the population of working age claiming unemployment benefit.
- The proportion of the population aged 65 and over claiming income support.

The indicators based on mortality rates, unemployment and income support are annually updateable, while the indicator of deprived households is taken from the 1991 census.

F.2   These four indicators were combined into a single index (the 'Arbuthnott index') using the method of z scores.

- The values of each indicator are available for every postcode sector in Scotland.
- The mean and standard deviation of each indicator were also calculated.
- The values of the indicators were standardised by taking the difference between the actual value and the mean and dividing by the standard deviation.
- The standardised values for the four indicators are then added together to provide an overall z score.
- This z score has then been used as the 'Arbuthnott index' of the key aspects of morbidity and life circumstances that influence the relative need for healthcare.

F.3   The value of this index ranges from -6.45 (the area with the lowest levels of morbidity and deprivation) to +16.06 (the area with the highest levels of morbidity and deprivation). The distribution of postcode sectors using this index is shown in Figure 3.5 in Chapter 3 of this report. The distribution is skewed with a small proportion of sectors having levels of morbidity and deprivation that are well above the national average.

F.4   The method used to arrive at the overall index effectively gives each of the four indicators equal weight. The sensitivity of the index to alternative weighting systems was examined, and the results are summarised in Table F.1. The numbers attached to the term 'index' in this table indicate the relative weighting applied to the four indicators (in the order shown at paragraph 1 above). For example, the term 'index2224' indicates that the first three indicators were given an equal weight of 20% each, and the fourth indicator was given a weight of 40%.

Table F.1: Correlation Coefficients Between Indices Based on Alternative Weighting Patterns

```
             index   index2224 index2242 index2422 index4222 index1144 index4411
-----------+-------------------------------------------------------------------
    index  |  1.0000

index2224  |  0.9954    1.0000

index2242  |  0.9944    0.9864    1.0000

index2422  |  0.9960    0.9875    0.9865    1.0000

index4222  |  0.9968    0.9902    0.9872    0.9924    1.0000

index1144  |  0.9845    0.9888    0.9907    0.9691    0.9723    1.0000

index4411  |  0.9851    0.9719    0.9681    0.9924    0.9908    0.9397    1.0000
```

The alternative indices based on different weighting patterns are very highly correlated with each other.

F.5   The 'Arbuthnott index' is also highly correlated with the Carstairs index though the four indicators used in Arbuthnott are quite different from those used in Carstairs. (The Carstairs index uses male unemployment, car ownership, overcrowded households, and social class.)

ANNEX G:
GLOSSARY OF ACRONYMS

ABBREVIATIONS USED FOR HEALTH BOARDS

A&C Argyll and Clyde
A&A Ayrshire and Arran
Bor Borders
D&G Dumfries and Galloway
Fife Fife
FV Forth Valley
Gram Grampian
GG Greater Glasgow
High Highland
Lan Lanarkshire
Loth Lothian
Ork Orkney
Shet Shetland
Tay Tayside
WI Western Isles

ACT	Additional Cost of Teaching
CHI	Community Health Index; the index of all patients registered at GP practices.
CMR	Continuous Morbidity Recording; measuring contacts with sample of GP practices.
COPPISH	Core Patient Profile Information in Scottish Hospitals
GDP	Gross Domestic Product
GMS	General Medical Services, covering services provided by general medical practitioners.
GROS	General Register Office for Scotland: provides population estimates and projections for Scotland. Also provides births and deaths data. Also responsible for the Census of Population in Scotland.
Health Board	Health Board: administrative area of Health Service in Scotland. The bodies to which allocations are made by the Scottish Executive Health Department.
HCHS	Hospital and Community Health Services.
ISD	Information and Statistics Division of the NHS in Scotland.
MLC	Morbidity and Life Circumstances
MYEs	Mid-Year Estimates (of the population). Produced by GRO (S) annually.

NHSiS	National Health Service in Scotland.
Out of Hours	For GPs, covers the period outside normal surgery hours, these services are intended to provide urgent medical treatment only
PAMs	Professions Allied to Medicine, e.g. psychology, chiropody, physiotherapy, speech therapy, occupational therapy.
PCS	Postcode sector.
SHARE	Scottish Health Authorities Revenue Equalisation: the name of the revenue allocation formula phased in in Scotland between 1978 and 1997/98.
SMPC	Scottish Medical Practice Committee: the professional body which decides the distribution of general medical practices.
SMR	Standardised Mortality Ratio: a measure of mortality rates
SMR(0-64)	Standardised Mortality Ratio 0-64 years: a measure of mortality rates for those under 65 years of age.
SEHD	Scottish Executive Health Department: the government department responsible for the NHS in Scotland